D0506918

OTHER BOOKS
BY THE EDITORS OF LIFE

LIFE NATURE LIBRARY

ECOLOGY

LIFE NATURE LIBRARY

ECOLOGY

by Peter Farb
and The Editors of LIFE

TIME INCORPORATED
NEW YORK

About Peter Farb

Peter Farb's name is by now familiar to LIFE Nature Library readers who have shared his experiences in *The Forest* and *The Insects*. His sensitive concern with the relationships among living things is expressed in the present volume, the product of a study which began in his boyhood and has continued with unabated enthusiasm through years of writing and traveling. A member of the Ecological Society, former secretary of the New York Entomological Society and a Fellow of the American Association for the Advancement of Science, Mr. Farb has written widely on nature subjects for magazines. He has published two very popular books, *Living Earth*, which concerns the ecology of the soil, and *Face of North America: The Natural History of a Continent*. Mr. Farb is also editor and co-author of the North American Nature Series published by Harper & Row, ecological volumes on the primary regions of the continent.

ON THE COVER: Waves lap the sand of the intertidal zone on a rocky shore in Oregon. Here, where land and sea meet, is one of the earth's most fascinating habitats—and often, too, one of its most varied.

Contents

TIME INC. BOOK DIVISION

Editor: NORMAN P. ROSS

Copy Director: WILLIAM JAY GOLD   *Art Director:* EDWARD A. HAMILTON

Chief of Research: BEATRICE T. DOBIE

EDITORIAL STAFF FOR "ECOLOGY"

Editor, LIFE Nature Library: MAITLAND A. EDEY

Assistant to the Editor: ROBERT MORTON

Copy Editor: PERCY KNAUTH

Designer: PAUL JENSEN

Staff Writers: DALE BROWN, DORIS BRY, MARY LOUISE GROSSMAN

Chief Researcher: MARTHA TURNER

Researchers: GERALD BAIR, PEGGY BUSHONG, SUE FREUDENHEIM, LeCLAIR LAMBERT,
PAULA NORWORTH, CAROL PHILLIPPE, MARJORIE PICKENS, ROXANNA SAYRE, PAUL SCHWARTZ,
NANCY SHUKER, IRIS UNGER, JOHN VON HARTZ

Picture Researchers: MARGARET K. GOLDSMITH, JOAN LYNCH

Art Associate: ROBERT L. YOUNG

Art Assistants: JAMES D. SMITH, MARK A. BINN, ERIC GLUCKMAN

Copy Staff: MARIAN GORDON GOLDMAN, JOAN CHAMBERS, DOLORES A. LITTLES

Publisher: JEROME S. HARDY

General Manager: JOHN A. WATTERS

LIFE MAGAZINE

Editor	*Managing Editor*	*Publisher*
EDWARD K. THOMPSON	GEORGE P. HUNT	C. D. JACKSON

The text for this book was written by Peter Farb, the picture essays by the editorial staff. The following individuals and departments of Time Inc. were helpful in producing the book: Eliot Elisofon, Fritz Goro, Dmitri Kessel, George Silk, Margaret Bourke-White and Ralph Crane, LIFE staff photographers; Doris O'Neil, Chief of the LIFE Picture Library; Clara Applegate of the TIME-LIFE News Service; and Content Peckham, Chief of the Bureau of Editorial Reference.

Introduction

ECOLOGY, in the next 10 or 20 years, may well become the most popular of sciences—a household word to those masses who today are ignorant of both the word and its meaning. This would not be surprising: In a world where the distances are rapidly shrinking through the increase in the attainable rates of speed, close contacts will be established between individuals, nations and civilizations where none was feasible a comparatively short time before.

Modern man becomes every day more conscious of the fact that his way of life is increasingly defined by his surroundings. In the past, these were restricted to the farm, the village, the city, the nation with its own cultural pattern. Today the surroundings of a growing number of people consist of the whole earth. The inhabitant of Western Europe knows that his existence, at least in part, depends on what happens, for example, in Asia; similarly, the American, particularly since World War II, has come to realize that his country cannot exist without its ties with Europe and the rest of the world.

It is not only a fact that the nations have become politically and culturally interdependent; they also codetermine, at least in part, each other's fates through what they undertake against nature in greed, shortsightedness and mere stupidity. Erosion in North and South America, in Africa, in the Near and Far East is a problem that concerns in equal measure the inhabitants of Iceland and the Solomon Islands. The extinction of beautiful animal species and the destruction of their habitat in distant parts of the world are, in the final reckoning, as much the concern of the Amsterdam bus driver as of the captain of New York's Staten Island ferry.

The growing realization of the close connection existing between all that happens on this small planet as a result of men's good will or the lack of it, or of nature's being kind or unkind, will not fail to arouse an interest in a science that occupies itself with the relationship between the living organism and its surroundings. It is much to be hoped, however, that such an aroused interest will not affect pure ecology as a science by diluting it to an amateurish half-science that appeals to the masses.

May the ecologists always be in a position to serve their science unhampered and may they be able to open the eyes of mankind, as this book attempts to do, not only to nature's delicate balance but also to the many and irremediable damages we inflict on our own Mother Earth every day and everywhere.

BERNHARD
Prince of the Netherlands
President of the World Wildlife Fund

1

The
All-embracing
Web

MODERN man likes to label the abounding world around him with the inclu-
sive word "nature," as if to imply that he can lump together everything
outside of his own skin—the multitudes of animals that run, hop, fly, crawl and
wriggle, the tens of thousands of plants that range from one-celled algae to lofty
redwoods, the diverse environments that range from perennial ice to tropical
forest. But for the other living things with whom man shares the planet, "nature" has many different meanings. To a fresh-water turtle, nature is simply its
home portion of a stream or pond; to a particular kind of fly, it is a hot spring,
and no spring of any other temperature will do; to a lowly plant like the rein-
deer moss, it is a rock slab in the tundra, and nowhere else.

Actually, there is no such thing as a "nature" that will satisfy all living things.
There are only homes or environments in which particular animals and plants
have become adapted to live through eons of natural selection. Whatever exists
outside of a particular creature's usual home—the food it is not adapted to
eat, the tree trunk it cannot bore into, the climate it cannot endure—is quite
unnatural to it. Appropriately enough, the study of living things in relation to
their environment and to each other is known as "ecology," a term coined

nearly 100 years ago from two Greek words that mean "the study of the home."

All living things are tied to their homes by a multitude of invisible strands. These strands are the various physical conditions found on the surface of this wrinkled and constantly changing planet. They are also found in the relationships—competition, cooperation, and even disinterested neutrality—between species living alongside one another. They include the interaction of all aspects of the environment: the soil the inhabitants walk on and burrow into, the air they breathe or fly in, the rainfall and light intensity they endure. Although the tenants of mountaintops, deserts and the open sea may appear to be sharply different in their shapes and ways of life, actually they all obey the same ecological laws. Some of these relationships are obvious: everyone knows that a pollinating honeybee interacts with a flower and helps it to produce seeds. But in the world of living things there are many interactions that are extremely subtle and obscure. Some, indeed, actually blur the distinction between a plant or an animal and its physical environment, for although living things take food and shelter from their environment, they also help to create it. Without the organic matter provided by living organisms, there could be no soil—only a collection of inert mineral particles. The soil that develops, in turn, is important in determining the kinds of plants that can grow in it, and plants, in their turn, support animals. The very atmosphere of this planet in its youth was probably different from what it is today: carbon dioxide and oxygen, both necessary for the origin of plant and animal life, are themselves produced today by plants and animals.

Man is the only creature that seemingly stands aloof from the interactions of living things, since he is able to make a home for himself almost anywhere in the world. But, impressive as his accomplishments are, man in reality has never left his ecological home. He still needs air to breathe, water to drink and suitable food—all of which he finds, creates or takes with him. It is his mastery of the technologies of fire, shelter and clothing that has enabled him to do this. Evolving from a prehuman ancestor that lived about two million years ago in the tropics, man has spread out over the whole face of the earth. But most of this spread has taken place only in the last few tens of thousands of years, and even today, the bulk of mankind still inhabits a limited land surface between 50 degrees north latitude and a few degrees south of the equator.

Most other kinds of life are even less widely dispersed, despite the fact that plants and animals seem to cram the globe. And this narrowness of distribution is vertical as well as horizontal, all life being confined to a thin veneer of the earth called the "biosphere." On land the biosphere extends down into the ground only as far as the roots of the deepest-growing trees. On the sea, although living things have been detected more than six miles down at the bottom of ocean trenches, almost all marine life is crowded into the top 500 feet of the ocean's surface. While some birds and insects may soar a few miles into the sky, they must inevitably come down again; the biosphere proper ascends only as high as the tops of the tallest trees—the 370-foot redwoods of California.

Thin as it is, this film is inhabited by upward of 1,300,000 different kinds of plants and animals, but very few of them have managed to make homes for themselves widely throughout the biosphere. Aside from man, the housefly appears to be the most far-ranging species, being found almost everywhere except the polar regions. This insect was originally confined to tropical latitudes, and experiments have demonstrated that its populations still flourish most successfully at a temperature of 77 degrees Fahrenheit. But it has been able to extend its range thanks to two adaptations: it can spend the cooler seasons of the year in a dormant state and it has adopted man's heated structures as its home. It has, in fact, been able to go everywhere that man has gone. Similarly, the common cockroach, bodylouse, pharaoh ant, house mouse and a few other species —all congeners with man—have invaded a diversity of environments. They have hurdled mountains and crossed seas with man; they arrived in their present homes with man and presumably will dwindle or disappear if man disappears.

Man and his congeners are the exceptions; all the other kinds of plants and animals occupy only limited places in the biosphere. There is no problem in explaining why monkeys, which are adapted to an arboreal life and feed upon the fruits of trees, should inhabit forests instead of deserts. Yet, it is difficult to understand completely their distribution. A rain forest in South America may be extremely similar to one in Africa, but the kinds of monkeys found in each are quite different: none of the African monkeys, for example, has a tail strong enough to grasp tree branches, whereas most of the South American ones do— and there is a similar rain forest in Australia that has no monkeys at all.

ALL animals and plants live where they do for a very good reason, and usually for several good reasons. If they are absent from an area that supports similar organisms, there are good reasons for that also. They may be prevented from getting there by such visible barriers as high mountain ranges or oceans, or by the invisible but equally insurmountable barriers of insufficient water, or the wrong kind of food, or subtle conditions of climate or soil. Sometimes they are inhibited by the presence of man, more often by the presence of another competing type which already fills the niche that the invader would otherwise occupy. Sometimes an animal or plant appears entirely suited to an environment and still is absent from it. This may be because of the absence of another organism on which it depends. The distribution of the aconite plant is a good example; it is wholly dependent on the bumblebee for cross-pollination, and as a result is never found beyond the range of the bumblebee itself.

For an understanding of the dispersal of certain organisms, it may be necessary to go back into the past. Living things themselves change as a result of the never-ending process of evolution through natural selection. In addition, the face of the earth is in constant change. The mountains that today form an impassable barrier may not have existed at all only a geological yesterday ago. It is less than 12,000 years since glacial ice retreated from the northern United States, pouring water into the oceans and thus altering the coastlines. As the glaciers retreated, new forests reclaimed the land, rivers changed their courses, lakes and bogs were formed. Changes such as these have always occurred and they have always brought about alterations in the distribution of living things. Many species of animals have migrated from continent to continent, moving across temporary land bridges. There are several species of mammals which originated in North America, walked across land now under the Bering Strait into Asia—and then became extinct here. The horse is one: it died out in North America as a native animal perhaps 10,000 years ago and did not reappear here until the Spanish conquistadors brought horses to Mexico in the 16th Century. The wild mustangs of the American West are the descendants of those Spanish imports.

The fact that most plants and animals have their unique haunts was impressed upon scientists at about the time that the far-reaching explorations of the globe started in the 15th Century, and explorers began bringing back almost unbelievable tales, as well as living examples, of strange beasts that existed in

35,000 YEARS AGO

■ Congoids
■ Mongoloids
■ Caucasoids
■ Capoids
■ Australoids

10,000 YEARS AGO

THE MIGRATIONS OF MAN

About 35,000 years ago, five races of Homo sapiens had evolved in Europe, Africa and Asia (top). These early men had large brains, a high degree of social organization, tools and weapons which made them superior hunters. In search of new hunting grounds, they spread to Australia, into the far north, over the Bering Strait, and down the Americas to Tierra del Fuego, following the game animals across Pleistocene land bridges to colonize new continents. When the last ice sheet retreated, about 10,000 years ago (above), the Mongoloids and Caucasoids had emerged as the two largest racial groups.

distant lands. Europeans were astonished by turkeys and guinea pigs, as well as by the exotic examples of humankind that were brought back from these voyages. But there was no adequate organization of the facts about the geographical distribution of animals until one was made in 1858 by Philip L. Sclater. This was modified and documented in 1876 by Alfred Russel Wallace, the brilliant co-author with Charles Darwin of the theory of evolution. Wallace recognized the world as divided into six land realms, with boundaries determined largely by impassable barriers of climate and topography. Although there have been subsequent minor shiftings of their boundaries by other scientists, Wallace's realms stand as the accepted biogeographical division of the planet. Maps usually show these realms separated by sharp lines, but in reality there was much intergrading between realms even in Wallace's time. Since then, man has further disrupted them by giving many species—the widespread starling and English sparrow are but two examples out of thousands—boosts over barriers into new realms where they have prospered. Nevertheless, the concept of realms is still valid to explain the historical biogeography of the earth. Although it can be seen most clearly in the distribution of land mammals and birds, it also holds true for many other groups of animals and for plants as well.

ZONE OF TRANSITION

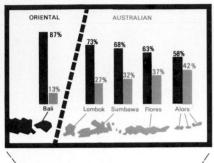

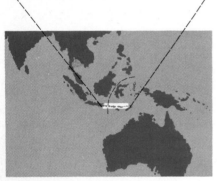

The zoogeographic lines that separate areas of different plant and animal populations are seldom as rigid as they appear on the map. As first drawn by Wallace, for example, the line separating the Oriental from the Australian realm ran between Bali and Lombok, two islands only 15 miles apart. However, recent studies have revealed that this part of the Malay Archipelago (bottom map) is actually a zone of gradual transition between the Australian and Oriental realms. How this is apparent in the bird population is indicated by the bars above the islands in the close-up at top representing the percentages of western (Oriental) and eastern (Australian) birds on each.

EACH realm possesses distinctive forms of life, unique to it and found nowhere else. The Nearctic realm—that is, North America down to approximately the Tropic of Cancer in Mexico—is distinguished by the presence of such animals as pronghorns, muskrats, bison, skunks and turkeys. The Oriental realm of India and Southeast Asia possesses the Indian elephant (quite different from the African elephant), the tiger, water buffalo, Malay tapir and gibbon. The Ethiopian realm—consisting of most of Africa except the northern fringe along the Mediterranean—has its own elephant, also the giraffe, zebra, gorilla and aardvark. The concept of realms can be seen clearly in the Malay Archipelago, where two of them meet: the Oriental realm, extremely rich in vertebrate animals, and the Australian realm, one of the most impoverished in vertebrates. In this crowded area, Wallace, noticing the differences in the plants and animals in the various islands, was able to draw a line on the map in such a way as to separate groups of living things from one another.

Although to the casual view there is little difference between the swarms of little islands that lie in the archipelago, they are, in fact, two separate realms that became physically isolated about 80 million years ago by a severe dislocation in the earth's crust. The line that Wallace drew, now known the world over as Wallace's Line, starts southeast of the Philippines, passing between the islands of Mindanao and Sangihe, then runs south between Borneo and Celebes, thence out into the Indian Ocean between Bali and Lombok. At one time it was thought that the fauna on both sides of the line were as sharply different as if they had been cut apart by a knife. However, it is now known that instead of a single precise line, there is actually a blurred band between the two realms—a land area appropriately given the name Wallacea—into which some representatives from both realms penetrate for a short distance.

As one proceeds eastward from the line, the number of species of animals from the Oriental realm drops off markedly; similarly, there is a diminishing number of Australian animals to the west of the line. A few of the Australian marsupials, or pouched mammals, have penetrated a short distance into Wallacea; an Oriental woodpecker has island-hopped slightly eastward of the line from Bali. Such Oriental animals as shrews, tarsiers, squirrels and pigs that have crossed the line eastward to the Celebes may all have been carried across by Melanesian man, who probably brought them along as food or as pets. But in many cases, the line has not become blurred at all. Bali and Lombok stand only about 15 miles apart on opposite sides of the line, but their faunas are amazingly different. Bali, in the Oriental realm, has been reached by squirrels and tigers from Asia, but these animals have gotten no further eastward. Lombok, on the other hand, has the Australian honey eaters, which are unknown in Bali. Elsewhere along the line the woolly opossum of Australia is found in the Celebes, but it has not crossed the few miles to Borneo; the cockatoos, an Australian family of birds, extend westward right up to the line but not beyond it.

SIMILAR barriers have shaped the course of life in the Nearctic, or North American realm. One, though not a permanent one, is the Bering Sea that separates Alaska and Siberia. The reason that many North American plants and animals are similar to Asiatic ones is that these two realms have been connected periodically by a land bridge during the recent ice ages and at least twice before during the early Tertiary and Upper Cretaceous, some 60 to 80 million years ago. Today the bridge no longer exists, submerged beneath the huge volumes of water poured into the oceans during the melting of the ice sheets, but it was more than once the scene of heavy traffic between the two continents. From Asia came many mammals, birds, reptiles and fishes now familiar in North America—and also, during the past 25,000 years, successive migrations of man. Migrations in the opposite direction were made by the camel, the horse and the tapir, all of which evolved in North America but invaded Asia.

North America was also connected to South America 60 to 70 million years ago, but the two realms were later separated by a water barrier and remained isolated for tens of millions of years until the present land bridge across southern Mexico, Nicaragua and Panama was formed. Before then, the mammals of South America were far more distinctive than they are today and they had almost nothing in common with those of North America or other continents. But as soon as movements of the earth's crust hurled up land bridges to North America, the tide of mammals began to flow both ways between the realms and each temporarily became richer than it had been previously: the North American families of land mammals increased from 27 to 34, South America's from 29 to 36. But the interchange resulted in duplication of animals that filled similar ecological roles, and such a situation of direct competition could not last long, for ultimately one of the competing forms wins out and the other becomes extinct or adapts to a different role. That is what happened—at present North America has only 23 families of land mammals (fewer than before the interchange), while South America has retained 30 families. The North American mammals—tapirs, llamas, peccaries, deer, foxes, otters, bears, raccoons, skunks and others—were much more successful in their invasion southward, and in many cases their descendants survive to this day. In fact, about half of the present mammals of South America are descendants of recent invaders from North America. By contrast the only southern mammals that have survived in North America are the porcupine, armadillo and opossum.

This then is the Nearctic realm, made up of bits and pieces largely from Eurasia and a scattering of South American forms, as well as the diversifications of native forms, such as the pocket gopher, which evolved wholly inside the Nearctic realm and has never been found outside of it. Today the Nearctic is richly populated by upwards of 650 species of birds, over 400 mammals, more than 200 reptiles, at least 140 amphibians, 150,000 insects and by other inverte-brates, and by plants that range from single-celled algae to lofty sequoias, as well as by almost all of the races of mankind. Each of these living things has its own distribution on the continent, and for an understanding of this distribution, scientists have found it useful to divide not only the Nearctic, but also all of Wallace's realms into smaller, more manageable categories known as biomes. A biome can be crudely described as a climatic zone. It has its own pattern of rainfall, its own maximum and minimum temperatures, its own seasons and its own changes of day length, all of which combine to produce a certain kind of vegetation—which, in turn, shelters a unique animal life.

The biomes on land are named for the predominant vegetation that has maintained itself in any given region. Each biome possesses its characteristic combination of plants and animals, each passes through a sequence of stages in its development, each tends to reach a point of approximate equilibrium with its environment that differs from the equilibrium reached in any other biome. Thus, a certain combination of temperature and soil and rainfall has produced a belt of coniferous forest across the northern portion of North America; another combination has produced a desert in the Southwest.

THE important part played by plants in determining the economy of a biome is demonstrated by the distribution of herds of large grazing mammals. These grazers are usually found in areas with an average rainfall of 12 to 30 inches a year, but which is unevenly spaced throughout the year. The grazers probably derive no benefits from this kind of semiarid climate, and in fact they suffer from it during the dry seasons. The reason they are most common where this kind of climate prevails is because the grasses on which the grazing herds feed are usually the dominant vegetation wherever such a rainfall pattern exists.

The Nearctic realm possesses all of the major terrestrial biomes except two—the tropical savannah of open land with a scattering of trees, and the tropical rain forest. At the roof of North America, south of the polar snow and ice, is the tundra biome. South of the tundra, and growing in a wide belt from the Atlantic Ocean nearly to the Pacific, is the green carpet of the northern coniferous forest biome. South of this coniferous belt, at about the Canadian border, the continent is broken vertically into several biomes by a complex of mountain barriers, wind currents, precipitation patterns and so forth. Proceeding westward across North America from the Atlantic Ocean, one first meets the deciduous forest biome, then the grassland biome, next the desert biome. The coniferous biome dips into some of these along the higher reaches of the Appalachians, Rockies, Cascades and Sierras and as a narrow coastal strip of temperate rain forest along the Pacific shore.

But even the division of the Nearctic realm into a number of biomes still results in areas of land too large and diverse to be fully meaningful in the examination of ecological relationships between living things. The deciduous forest, for example, that ranges from southern New York into the southern Appalachians (composed largely of oaks and chestnuts, before the latter were decimated by a blight) is considerably different from the deciduous forest in the Ozarks of southern Missouri and Arkansas, composed largely of oaks and hickories. And not only are many of the species of trees different, but so are the other kinds of plants as well as the animals that live there.

As one narrows one's area of view even further, one finds that the oak-chestnut forest still encompasses too diverse an area for meaningful examination. Depending upon the factors of temperature, moisture, degree of slope, north or south exposure, elevation, soil or man's influence, the vegetation clothes a single mountain in a mosaic of different combinations: fir forests, grassy balds, heath balds, oak forests and many others. Clearly a whole mountain is still subject to subdivision, for every one of the forest combinations on its hillsides is populated by its own combination of mammals, birds, reptiles, amphibians, insects and other invertebrates, all in intimate relationship with that particular kind of forest. It is at the level of these restricted areas that the interactions of climate, shelter, food and competition at last reveal themselves significantly. Every such area is a "habitat," the address of an organism, the place where it lives.

WITHIN the confines of a habitat, it is possible to determine why living things live where they do. An animal with a highly specialized diet can live only in a habitat where the food it eats grows. The koala bear of Australia feeds exclusively on eucalyptus leaves and thus can live only in habitats where these trees grow. Similarly, giant pandas of Asia must live where their food plant, the bamboo, is found. In other cases the relationship of an animal to its habitat is much more complex. Everyone knows that only in the Arctic can a polar bear be seen in the wild. Yet why should not the polar bear be found elsewhere, especially in the similarly cold Antarctic, where it is completely absent?

It is not warm climate alone that prevents polar bears from penetrating southward, for they survive quite well in zoos in the United States. More important is that certain conditions to which polar bears have become adapted in the Arctic are lacking elsewhere. They live only where all three essential conditions —cold water, marine food (primarily seals, but also young walruses, fish and stranded whales) and drift ice—exist at the same time. If one of these factors is absent, so is the polar bear. All three conditions exist also in the Antarctic, but the polar bear has never been able to get there; its route would have to take it through the temperate and tropic zones, where the cold water and drift ice are both lacking.

Wherever one looks—on land, along the shore or in the sea—living things similarly have their proper places. Often the balance of an organism with its environment allows some flexibility for change, but sometimes it is critical. As the habitat changes, so will the animal life it harbors—as was seen after the African savannah south of Lake Edward in the Congo was included in the Albert National Park. Formerly, this area of low grasses supported a wide variety of antelopes and carnivores, intimately linked to their habitat. But burning by natives, which had served to prevent tree growth, was now prohibited; furthermore, a severe outbreak of locusts denuded the land. The vegetation under these circumstances changed rapidly to scrub thickets—and the mammal population changed too. In only nine years the numbers of two kinds of antelopes dropped from 25,000 animals to 4,200, and there was a corresponding decrease in such carnivores as lions and hyenas. The tree growth favored the elephants, and they increased markedly. Large numbers of them invaded the park and they destroyed the trees. The result was that the vegetation reverted to low grasses once again. Now the wheel has turned full circle: the population of antelopes has soared to its previous levels.

In the case of some fresh-water fishes, the section of the stream they inhabit is determined largely by the amount of dissolved oxygen in the water, a necessity for their breathing. Some species, such as the brook trout, require large amounts of dissolved oxygen and must inhabit the upper reaches of streams where the

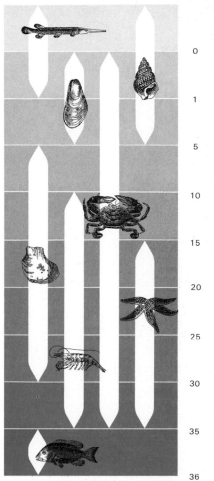

SALINITY:
PARTS PER THOUSAND

0

1

5

10

15

20

25

30

35

36

TIDEWATER ZONES

An estuary, the area where a river's fresh water pours into the sea and which is churned by the tides, is divided into a series of habitats by the varying salinity of its water. Degrees of salinity form invisible but definite boundaries for the creatures living in an estuary. Thus the river-dwelling gar can venture only a little way downstream; the fresh-water snail, on the other hand, is given some protection from greater salinity by its shell. The mussel's niche is narrow, but crabs, oysters and shrimp are all adapted to wide variations. Starfish cannot tolerate less than 1.5 per cent of salinity, and snappers must live in the open sea.

water is aerated by pouring over rocks; other species, such as some catfishes, can inhabit the lower sluggish sections of streams where the oxygen content is low. A study of the fishes inhabiting a stream in Florida revealed that they too were precisely distributed in various portions of the stream, according to the differing oxygen content of the water. The source of this stream was two springs, and at the point where they flowed from the ground, the water was nearly devoid of oxygen—a mere fifth of a part of oxygen per million parts of water. The only species that lived there were two kinds of gambusia, a molly and the least killifish. As the water flowed downstream it began to pick up oxygen from the atmosphere and from water plants, and the oxygen content gradually increased to about one part per million. A different killifish, the redfin, was adapted to live in a habitat with this amount of oxygen; the species that lived upstream were absent. As the stream flowed on, the oxygen content continued to increase, and other species of fishes appeared and disappeared, depending upon their oxygen need. Only when the oxygen content reached between 1.3 and 2 parts per million was the stream inhabited by large-mouth bass, sunfish and pickerel.

THE particular place of an animal within its habitat—its relation to its environment, its food, its partners and enemies—is known as its niche. Animals usually evolve in such a way as to adapt more and more closely to their particular niches, as can be seen in the many adaptations in the feet of birds. The arrangement of the toes, the length of the legs, the presence or absence of webbing and other specializations determine whether a bird will scratch on the ground for seed like a quail, use its feet to grasp prey as a hawk does, paddle like a duck, wade like a heron or brace itself on a tree trunk like a woodpecker.

To an animal, the local microclimate that prevails in its niche is much more important to it than the broad classifications of climate used by meteorologists. A little forest rodent is scarcely influenced by the atmospheric conditions several feet above the ground in a forest clearing; much more important to it are the temperature, humidity and light intensity at ground level, underneath the shelter of shrubs and weeds. Even within a niche, there are many subtle variations and they become more pronounced the smaller an organism is. A rock exposed to the sun may influence the life of a plant as significantly as a mountain chain influences man by altering wind and moisture patterns and by retaining heat. That is why a tropical plant, growing in a sheltered spot in a northern garden, may survive for weeks after killing frost has destroyed a similar plant growing in an unprotected part of the same garden.

At first glance, it may not seem terribly urgent to man whether a particular species inhabits the sunlit or shaded side of a boulder, or even whether different kinds of periwinkles find separate ecological niches only a few inches from each other on a rocky shore. Yet the presence or absence of forms of life filling these niches will determine the success of other species of life associated with them, and these in turn will have a marked effect upon still others. No organism lives without affecting its environment and being affected in turn. And it has been increasingly demonstrated that the intricate strands that form the ecological web of life also enmesh mankind. "In defying nature, in destroying nature, in building an arrogantly selfish, man-centered, artificial world, I do not see how man can gain peace or freedom or joy," writes the noted ecologist Marston Bates in *The Forest and the Sea*. "I have faith in man's future, faith in the possibilities latent in the human experiment: but it is faith in man as a part of nature . . . faith in man sharing life, not destroying it."

GRASS AND ISOLATED TREES ABLE TO STAND LONG DRY SPELLS MARK TROPICAL SAVANNAS IN AFRICA, SOUTH AMERICA AND AUSTRALIA

Earth's Many Realms

With few exceptions, land plants and animals are quite local in their distributions over the globe. They have been kept in their areas by many factors. There are physical barriers—mountains, seas, rivers. Just as important, there is the invisible barrier of climate, determining, through the adaptations plants and animals must make to it, the interlocking life—and even the look—of entire regions.

The Geography of Life

When, in response to the great upsurge of zoological discoveries in the 19th Century, naturalists analyzed the facts they had collected about the seemingly haphazard distribution of animals throughout the world, a surprising pattern emerged: animals of widely different varieties were grouped in broad regional units. Each unit showed faunal similarities, but each also contained animals found nowhere else—Australia, for example, was rich in marsupials, and South America supported such strange placental mammals as the tree sloth and the related anteater. So distinctive were these units that it was possible to divide the world into six major zoological realms which, with minor revisions of boundaries, still stand today and are delineated on the maps presented on these and the following pages.

The zoological realms coincide approximately with the continents. Differences in their fauna are to a large extent the result of the presence or absence of physical barriers to animal dispersal—mountains, rivers or seas—and by the relation of the continents to each other, especially in the distant past. Thus, although North America and South America are today connected to each other by land, the fauna of North America resembles much more that of northern Asia, to which it was once connected across the Bering Strait. South America, on the other hand, until approximately 15 million years ago was an island continent like Australia, which developed a fauna all its own. But when North America and South America were joined, animals that could successfully pass through the narrow funnel of the Isthmus of Panama did so: tapirs, for example, left their original North American home for the southern continent, in which they are still found today. The world's only other tapirs live in Central America and many thousands of miles away in Southeast Asia, to which they migrated across the arctic bridge that vanished long ago.

WILD TURKEY

TINAMOUS

GUINEA PIG

MOCKINGBIRD

RED-EYED VIREO

NEARCTIC REALM

OVENBIRD

RATTLESNAKE

BISON

SKUNK

MUSKRAT

TIGER SALAMANDER

PRONGHORN

TOUCAN

NEOTROPICAL REALM

HUMMINGBIRDS

HOWLER MONKEY

TAPIR

SLOTH

RHEA

ANTEATER

ZOOGEOGRAPHIC REALMS
OF THE EASTERN HEMISPHERE

ROE DEER

OLD WORLD WARBLER

DORMOUSE

HEDGE SPARROW

WATER MOLE

OLD WORLD FLYCATCHER

HEDGEHOG

OSTRICH

SABLE ANTELOPE

SECRETARY BIRD

GUINEA FOWL

GORILLA

AFRICAN
ELEPHANT

ETHIOPIAN REALM

HIPPOPOTAMUS

GIRAFFE

ZEBRA

AARDVARK

LION

PALAEARCTIC REALM

ARGALI

WILD ASS

PEACOCK

ORANGUTAN

GIBBON

INDIAN TIGER

INDIAN ELEPHANT

ORIENTAL REALM

FAIRY BIRD

TREE SHREW

GAVIAL

JUNGLE FOWL

AUSTRALIAN REALM

KOALA

FLYING PHALANGER

BIRD OF PARADISE

PLATYPUS

CASSOWARY

KANGAROO

KIWI

TUATARA

The Biomes

Why do animals live where they do? Zoological realms provide only partial answers to this question; hence the concept of the biome, a smaller region. In the biome, now generally defined as an area controlled on land by climate, and distinguished on land or in the sea by the dominance of certain types of plants or animals, ecological relationships can be closely studied. Thus, for example, in colder regions a coniferous forest biome stands revealed: a forest dominated by cold-resisting evergreens whose superior adaptations and utilization of the available light, water and mineral nutrients limit the growth of other types of plants—and strongly influence the animal population.

Coniferous Forest

Young spruces and firs begin to crowd out deciduous aspens in the coniferous forest biome. Evergreens dominate this broad belt, some 400 to 800 miles wide, which stretches across Canada, Alaska and Eurasia and, farther south, covers high mountains. Moose are found in the northern area, mule deer *(below)* in the western mountains. One bird, the red crossbill, has a beak so specialized for picking seeds from cones that it can live only here.

Tropical Forest

The rampant green growth of a Brazilian mountainside, nurtured by abundant rains and simmering warmth, is characteristic of but one kind of tropical forest. The diverse forests which make up this ancient biome, whether South American, Asian or African, are stratified into conspicuous stories—some having as many as five levels. Each story is formed by the crowns of trees and shrubs of many different species growing closely together. And each story may shelter plants—from low-lying ferns to aerial epiphytes—and animals different in habits and adaptations from those living directly above or below.

Temperate Deciduous Forest

In temperate areas, where seasons change from summer heat to winter cold and where there is sufficient precipitation, the natural ground cover is forest—and forest of a particular kind. These are conditions that favor the growth, above all other plants, of deciduous trees. Named for their habit of shedding their leaves in the fall, they include such varieties as elms, maples and beeches. The canopies they form affect all life in their shade, and the deciduous forest biome of eastern North America, temperate Europe and eastern Asia harbors many of the familiar plants and animals of the North Temperate Zone.

25

The Reef

A watery Eden of clear blue, blue-green and green, the reef is a flourishing marine biome. Like this section of Australia's Great Barrier Reef, it occurs where waters are warm and shallow, and builds up slowly from the calcareous remains of organisms like the polyps below. Self-sufficient worlds, reefs support a variety of plants and animals, from algae to clouds of brightly colored fishes—which in turn attract both fish-eating birds and larger fishes from the deep ocean waters just beyond.

The Desert

In contrast to the watery reef is the arid desert biome: hummocks of vegetation rising from sun-singed sands. Deserts cover about one fifth of the earth's surface. Controlled by climate, desert plants have developed such modifications as tough "skins" and reduced foliage to prevent evaporation and withstand heat. Large mammals are scarce, but rodents like the desert rat above abound. Many are nocturnal in habit: night offers concealing darkness, coolness—and often dew.

The Tundra

Caribou are among the largest mammals of the Canadian tundra, adapted for life in this far northern region. The tundra biome begins where the coniferous forest ends and runs to the barrier of permanent snows and ice in Eurasia and North America. It also occurs in modified form on high mountains. Its principal vegetation of lichens, mosses and grasses makes the most of a brief growing season in which the subsoil never thaws completely, and provides food for the caribou, whose trails are marked by the grim mementoes of wolves (*right*).

The Rocky Shore

Beyond the carpet of flowers opposite lies the rocky shore, a rigorous biome. Pounded by waves, exposed by tides to sun and air, this is yet an area in which life abounds. Extending from high to below tide levels, it is divided into three major zones. Snails prevail in the upper zone, acorn barnacles and masses of brown algae in the middle or intertidal region, and kelps with long stalks and ribbonlike branches at the bottom—each reflecting a tolerance to varying degrees of exposure.

Grassland

A sea of grass rolling toward distant mountains typifies the grassland biome often found in the interiors of continents. Climate is a controlling factor: rainfall is insufficient to support trees but high enough to keep deserts from forming. The result is a variety of tall, medium and short grasses which

reflect the gradient of rainfall—as in the United States, with its zones of progressively shorter growth westward to the Rockies. Grassland soil is rich in humus in areas of taller grass, since leaves die at the end of each growing season and decay quickly. Man with his agriculture and livestock has destroyed much of the world's grassland biome, and few large patches survive. In earlier days, they supported big herds of grazing mammals and colonies of rodents like the prairie dog.

The Ocean

Vast and in many places seemingly thinly populated, the sea is actually a reservoir of life—filled in different regions and at different times with billions of animals and plants so small that they cannot be seen by the human eye. These tiny, passively floating and weak-swimming organisms, the plankton, constitute one of the lowest links on the food chain. Together with the nekton, or actively moving organisms—the fishes, squids, whales, seals and porpoises and fish-eating birds—they make up the oceanic plankton-nekton biome. Here such factors as light, pressure, temperature, salinity and oxygen content of the water determine the make-up of the various plant and animal communities. With its potential as a source of food for mankind relatively unexplored, this biome, perhaps more than any other, is receiving the concentrated attention of ecologists seeking ways to develop—while conserving—its rich abundance.

32

AN OVERTURNED ROCK on the seashore exposes clusters of acorn barnacles whose flat cones, toughened
with lime, are securely cemented
to the surface. Under tidal cover
they open up and draw in plankton.

2

Coexistence in the Community

IN *The Origin of Species*, to demonstrate "how plants and animals remote in the scale of nature are bound together by a web of complex relations," Charles Darwin took a close look at red clover and its relationship with the bumblebees which pollinate it. The result was an ecological classic.

Darwin discovered that bumblebees, because of their long tongues, are the only insects which can effectively pollinate the deep red clover flowers. From this he argued that the success of red clover in England can be attributed to the fact that bumblebees are so prevalent there. He then went on to quote an authority who had found that there were more bumblebee nests in the vicinity of villages and towns than elsewhere because field mice, which eat bumblebee combs and larvae, are scarce around towns. And why are field mice scarce? Because towns usually harbor large numbers of cats which prey upon the field mice and keep their population down. Here a German scientist took up the argument: cats, he said, were thus proved responsible for the prevalence of red clover in England; red clover, a staple food of British cattle, could be ecologically linked to the British navy, whose staple diet was bully beef; hence cats could be given the ultimate credit for Britain's dominance as a world power.

Sir Thomas Huxley then went even one step further: he suggested, half-humorously, that since old maids were well known to be the principal protectors of cats throughout all England, the fact that Britannia ruled the waves might logically—and ecologically—be traced right back to the cat-loving tendencies of her spinsters.

Darwin's cat-and-clover story, with its embellishments, is undoubtedly overdrawn, but it does demonstrate the far-reaching ecological relationships that bind together an incongruous assortment of plants and animals. And the wondrous diversity of living things in such a community, the subtlety of their adaptations, their endlessly intriguing behavior—all these appealing things about the world of nature are largely but means to the end of obtaining a portion of the food energy that flows from one member of a community to another. A forest may seem hushed or the pond surface may be broken only by the dancing motes of insects and the occasional splash of a fish, yet every member of these communities is hard at work producing or consuming energy.

Sunlight pours alike upon the forest's soaring trees and the minute algae in a woodland pond, offering its energy to be converted into green growth through the process of photosynthesis. Here is where the energy of the sun becomes available to the community. Much of the energy is used by the plants in their own growth, development and reproduction; most of it is simply wasted. But the energy that is retained in the structures of the plants themselves becomes the reservoir of energy upon which the traffic of the entire community depends —hence the plants are known as the producers. A deer that browses on the buds and tender bark of the trees may be the first, or "primary," consumer. It expends energy, of course, in moving from tree to tree and in stretching to reach the branches, but it accumulates more energy than it expends, and thus it, too, becomes a source for another consumer of this same energy that came originally from the sun. A mountain lion may be the secondary consumer, preying upon the deer or another plant eater and thus achieving its energy secondhand. In time the mountain lion will die and some of its energy may end up in the crop of a vulture; the bulk of it, however, will probably go into the soil where it will be broken down by bacteria and fungi into simple nutrients for use again by plants to produce more energy and keep the cycle going.

THE channels of this constant flow of energy through the community are known as food chains. Actually, "chain" is a somewhat misleading term, conjuring up as it does an orderly set of links, whereas the whole matter of who eats whom may be extraordinarily complex. A beetle may feed on a wide variety of plants; in turn, any one of an assortment of birds, spiders and other insects may feed upon that beetle; these predators themselves have a host of enemies, any one of which may form a link in the chain. And it would be more accurate to say that each of these links is really an energy transformer, using some of the energy originally captured by the plants for its own maintenance and reproduction, and passing the balance of it on to another link in the chain. In a luxuriant woodland or a teeming coral reef, food chains assume gigantic proportions of complexity; but in a restricted place, such as a cave, they are displayed more starkly, making it relatively easy to understand the principles under which they operate.

The most abundant inhabitants of a cave are often bats, which use them as regular daytime dwellings or as places for hibernation. The floor beneath the cave roof to which the bats cling is usually covered by a deep deposit of droppings. The droppings are rich in nutrients, and in the dim light of the cave where the bats sleep a few kinds of lower plants can grow, such as molds, lichens and mosses. These plant producers furnish food for a number of different kinds of insects. One of the most common is the so-called cave cricket, which is found also in other dark places, such as the cellars of human habitations. Other invertebrates include springtails, beetles, moths, centipedes, harvestmen, mites and spiders, which either feed directly upon the meager plant growth or prey upon those invertebrates that do. In addition, there are various bat parasites—blind and wingless relatives of the bedbug and a variety of flies. All of this limited community of life depends, in the last analysis, upon the presence of the bats. They are the links to the outside world, since they bring energy into the cave in the form of night-flying insects they have eaten while foraging. If the bats abandon the cave during the summer in favor of a hollow tree or if they become dormant and cease to feed during the winter, then their droppings no longer accumulate. The molds that grow on them cease to thrive, the crickets and other invertebrates starve, and so do their predators, the spiders and others. Since the bats no longer bring in energy from the sunlit world, the economy of the cave gradually shuts down.

ACTUALLY, even this food chain of so restricted an environment as a small cave has been much simplified for illustration. There are other things going on in the cave which complicate the whole picture. A small amount of energy, for example, is washed into the cave by streams, rainstorms and springs in the form of particles of organic matter from plants that grow in the sunlight. Air drafts waft in fungus and bacteria spores, and seeds are often carried in by a variety of animals that make temporary use of the cave. Out of this maze of interactions, three primary food chains can be detected: the predator chain, which has a sequence from plant producers to generally small plant eaters and then to larger carnivores; the parasite chain, which leads from large animals to the smaller ones which parasitize them and thus rob their energy store; and the saprophyte chain, which is carried on largely in the soil and passes from dead plants and animals into microorganisms. And these chains, too, are themselves interwoven into a tight-knit pattern, a food web with a bewildering number of interlaced strands. It is virtually impossible to pluck out a single food chain from a community, since each link in the chain has living links leading back to other animals and plants.

As one examines a food chain in terms of the animals and plants that constitute it, it soon becomes apparent that these forms can be arranged into what is called a pyramid of numbers. At the bottom of it are multitudes of energy-producing plants, then a smaller number of herbivores that feed upon them, then a still smaller number of primary carnivores followed by an even smaller number of secondary carnivores. The animals at the top of the heap, the final consumers, are usually the largest in the community. The animal species at the bottom of the chain, the primary consumers, are usually the smallest but most abundant members of the community. For a community to support a single fisher at the apex of the pyramid, for example, several pine martens are needed for the fisher to prey upon; these martens need an even greater number of squirrels for *their* food; the squirrel population requires energy in the form of a tremendous number of nuts from trees.

The fisher or other predator ordinarily does not eat itself out of its food supply, since it rarely can increase as rapidly as its prey. Despite large numbers of

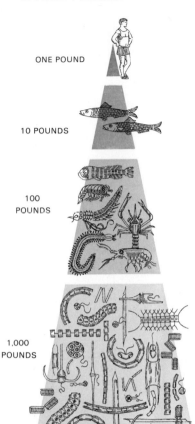

A FOOD PYRAMID

ONE POUND

10 POUNDS

100 POUNDS

1,000 POUNDS

For a man to gain a pound, the sea must produce half a ton of living matter. This is dramatically diagramed above, where the man at the top of the pyramid represents the final consumer in a marine food chain. The base of the pyramid is formed by the plant plankton—the so-called producers—which trap the sun's energy through photosynthesis. They are eaten by small animals at the next tier in the pyramid, and these in turn are consumed by the fish of the third tier. With each transfer of material, there is an approximately 10-to-one loss in bulk. Thus 1,000 pounds of plant plankton produce 100 pounds of animal plankton, which, in turn, yield 10 pounds of fish—the amount needed by the man to put on one pound.

predatory lions on the plains of Africa, tremendous herds of their primary prey, zebras and antelopes, nevertheless graze there. In a farmer's barn one might expect to find a roughly similar relationship of cats to rats and mice—except that in this case, in order to keep the rats and mice down to absolute minimum levels, the farmer subsidizes by feeding a larger number of predators—i.e., cats —than could ordinarily survive solely on the rats and mice.

In addition to the pyramid of numbers, there is also a pyramid of energy involved in a food chain. From the bottom of the pyramid, where energy is available in abundance to the producers, energy dissipates steadily; in the final consumer at the top it is stored only in meager amounts. This loss of energy from link to link is in the form of heat, caused by normal animal activities, and though it is partly offset by the increased efficiency of energy conversion into living protoplasm, it nonetheless limits the links in any food chain to rarely more than five.

IN the past, biologists as well as laymen applied the term "beneficial" or "injurious" to various links in the food chains. The red-shouldered hawk, for instance, has been acclaimed as a beneficial bird because it normally preys on rodents, which in turn feed upon man's crops; the goshawk, on the other hand, has been shot because it plucks an occasional chicken from the barnyard or preys upon a game bird which man himself desires to prey upon with a shotgun. This unsophisticated and very man-oriented view of food chains has now been replaced by a new understanding that, to maintain a healthy community, all of the links must be present, regardless of whether they seem immediately favorable or unfavorable to man's aims. As the intricacies of the community are investigated ever more deeply, it soon becomes obvious that it is impossible to distinguish friend from foe, a beneficial animal from an injurious one.

An excellent example can be seen in many woodlands of eastern North America. Assuming that trees are beneficial to man, it follows that one must condemn as injurious the Cecropia moth, which in its caterpillar stage feeds on an enormous number of tree leaves. Logically, one would next assume that any species that preys upon the Cecropias must be beneficial. But in one area where Cecropias were studied, it was found that among the animals that prey upon them—including six species of insects—are two species of mice. Mice are sometimes extremely destructive to young trees, yet here they are also destroying the enemy of the trees, the injurious Cecropia. Which side of the ledger should they be placed on—friend or foe?

As for the six species of insects which attack the Cecropia caterpillars, it might be assumed that they all are beneficial. But two of these parasites are in turn parasitized by secondary parasites, which, if one continues the same logic, must inevitably be classified as injurious. Parasitism, however, is a complex subject indeed: some of these injurious secondary parasites also attack other parasites which man has regarded as being injurious. Under certain conditions, therefore, these "injurious" secondary parasites can be "beneficial." Delving even deeper into the life history of only one of these particular "injurious-beneficial" parasites, one learns that it is attacked by still another, tertiary parasite. By this time, it is impossible to decide whether this last parasite should be regarded as beneficial or injurious. In short, a community is composed of so many gears meshed with other gears that it is futile to attempt to label any one of the gears as friend or foe, beneficial or injurious. Nevertheless, man attempts to do just that by recklessly spreading poisons across the landscape, by placing bounties upon the heads of certain predatory mammals and birds and by attempting to manage communities so that they will produce the maximum number of game species which he can then hunt. In so doing, he may well defeat himself, for the community is a complex and delicate piece of machinery and tossing a single monkey wrench into it can cause immense damage to the entire mechanism.

Most communities are in a constant state of change, their make-up varying not only from season to season, but also from day to day, even from minute to minute. The daytime animals give way to nocturnal ones at dusk, and the roles are reversed again at daybreak. The spring flowers fade and die to be replaced by summer and then by autumn species. Certain animals become inactive and invisible at various times of the day and the year. Most of these shifts are expressed by the presence or the temporary absence of certain species from the community. Birds arrive in the spring and depart in the fall; bears and other hibernators stage their seasonal disappearances and reawakenings. Rarely does a species become entirely eliminated except through cataclysmic earth changes or the hand of man.

A community emphasizes the fact that different kinds of animals and plants usually live together in a reasonably orderly manner, not just strewn over the landscape haphazardly. Each community is the result of a fascinating and complex interplay of biological, physical and historical forces, and these same forces are at work whether the particular place is a bare rock, inhabited only by a crusty growth of lichens and a few mosses and insects, or a luxuriant coral reef, alive with an astonishing diversity of animals. Each possesses adaptations that enable it to maintain itself at near self-sufficiency, to withstand adversity, to find at least the minimum necessities for life. Various members of the community feed upon or parasitize one another; some species have developed beneficial relationships that enable them to be more successful; many species are seemingly oblivious of the other members. Nevertheless, each member of the community has made numerous subtle adjustments to the other members and to its physical surroundings.

A COMMUNITY may consist largely of animals, as in a coral reef; or of plants, as in a spruce-fir forest; or, as in grasslands, it may abound in both plants and animals. The community centering around a bed of kelp floating off the shore of California may shelter several kinds of fishes, some 40 species of invertebrate animals, numerous algae, protozoans and bacteria, and even such a large animal as the sea otter, which finds sanctuary there from killer whales which roam the coastal waters. And there are, of course, communities within communities. A hole in a tree is an environment not only for a specialized community of birds such as woodpeckers, screech owls and nuthatches, but also for reptiles, mosquitoes and other forms of life that may use it as a home. Nor are communities entirely independent: although some may appear to be self-sufficient, most require a connection with communities elsewhere. Thus an oyster bed must have a suitable sea bottom, the necessary amount of salts in the water and the correct temperature—but this is not enough, it must also have circulating water that brings to the oysters food from other communities nearby.

Most communities blend gradually into each other, but sometimes there are abrupt boundaries between them. The borderline in any case is a zone of tension, an "ecotone," as it is known to ecologists. The banks of a stream that runs through a meadow, the edge between a forest and a grassland—these are blurred boundaries where there is usually a transition zone, with sparse outposts of each community enduring inside the territory of the other until finally they can penetrate no farther because conditions for living have become intolerable for them. This intermixing of communities makes the border areas particularly interesting. Ornithologists know that the best way to see a large variety of birds is to walk the ecotones. One study in Texas revealed that the margins of a forest clearing had almost twice as many individual birds, representing 41 per cent more species, as the interior of the woodland itself. By inhabiting the forest-edge ecotone, birds get the best of two worlds—insect food and grass for nest lining in the meadow, and a chance to escape from enemies into the protection of the woods. The reason many people have large populations of birds in their gardens is not only that they hang up feeders, but also that they have provided shrubs and trees, lawns and flower beds, artificial pools and the shelters of man's own habitations—in short, a variety of ecotones within a small area.

MANY surveys have been made of the numbers of plants and animals that make up a community, but analyses of these are difficult. Different collecting methods are used which make comparisons unreliable, and some of the inconspicuous inhabitants often escape notice altogether. Nevertheless, as one glances down a list of the number of larger animals in various communities, several generalizations emerge. Most communities seem to hold a population of large animals that ranges between 60 and 140 species, although in teeming marine communities and in some tropical forests one might find considerably more. In the Arctic, plant species usually outnumber the animals; in tropical rain forests, the opposite is usually the rule. Only a few of the different kinds of organisms present in a community exert major control because of their large size, their abundance or even their behavior. In a prairie community in Africa or in central North America, the grasses are so abundant that they govern the whole ecological relationship; along a rocky seacoast, the ability of barnacles and mussels to attach themselves firmly to bare and wave-swept rock is a major factor in the success of the other inhabitants.

Clearly, therefore, there are dominant species in any community. An oak tree in a forest manufactures energy from the sun, provides shade and thus prevents the drying out of the forest soil, curtails the movement of air and performs many other services for the forest dwellers. An earthworm living in the same forest passes the leaf litter endlessly through its digestive system, thus

HERONS SORTED OUT INTO SEPARATE NICHES

The five kinds of herons shown at right live on the same shoal in Florida and like the same food. Because they have evolved adjustments in their behavior, in their use of space and in ways of hunting food, they can live side by side, each in a separate niche in the shallow-water community, without crowding each other out.

Starting at the left is the green heron, which simply waits passively for fish to appear in the shallows around the prop roots of mangrove trees. Next to it is the more active Louisiana heron, which wades out a little way to seek its food. The snowy egret skims the water, ruffling it with a foot to flush out prey. Most elaborate of all, the reddish egret first stirs up the water to alarm the fish, then spreads its wings to form a canopy which gives the fish a brief illusion of security before they are speared by its bill. The great blue heron, because of its size, can wade out into quite deep waters to reach a food supply that is not readily available to its smaller and shorter-legged heron cousins.

40

GREEN HERON

LOUISIANA HERON

improving the physical and chemical properties of the soil. Both the oak and the earthworm play their part in the economy of the forest—but while the earthworm is important, the oak is vital, for the entire make-up of that particular forest community is controlled by the oaks and their associated trees.

The oak is the *dominant* of its forest, and only those animals and plants capable of enduring the conditions it creates can inhabit the woods over which it holds sway. In other forests, other kinds of dominant trees may give direction to the entire community, but in all communities, there are compartments within compartments. Closer to the ground, the shrubs proliferate, and only certain forest dwellers are tenants in their subcommunity; below them, the subdominant is the lowly herb. In the same forest, a lichen may be the subdominant on a patch of sunlit rock, mosses in a shaded spot, ferns along a stream. Each of these subdominants must be able to tolerate the conditions imposed by the oak dominant, yet each of the subdominants in turn modifies the community still further. The various secondary groupings of plants and animals within the community form minor aggregations known as societies: a rotting log in the oak forest becomes the focus for a society of numerous kinds of fungi, ants, termites, beetles, millepedes, centipedes and snails.

One of the major problems which members of the same or different species in the community must settle is the apportionment of living space. For many animals, the problem is solved simply: they occupy different niches and are in no competition for space or food. A bird of the treetops may never cross the path of a different species that lives on the forest floor. But for birds of the same species that occupy the same niche, adjustment is a delicate matter and a host of compromises must be worked out through the formation of nesting and feeding territories. The outlining of territories is thus a major theme in a community. The beaver marks off the boundaries of its territory by scent and the use of sound warnings. The breeding grounds of seals are a mosaic of invisible little domains—breeding areas, places where bachelors gather, special places where the pups play. In the Central American rain forests, the behavior of the large howler monkeys is seemingly chaotic. Yet a careful study of about 400 of these monkeys that inhabited some 4,000 acres on Barro Colorado Island in Panama revealed that each monkey was attached to one of 23 clans and each clan claimed a definite territory outlined by some physical feature, such as a large tree or a rise in the terrain. And although the casual human observer could detect little difference between the bands of howlers, each clan actually remained within—

SNOWY EGRET   REDDISH EGRET   GREAT BLUE HERON

and defended—the invisible boundaries of its territory. When two clans on the move accidentally approached a borderline at the same time, a vigorous howling was set up until one or both clans retreated.

In the unbelievably complex web of the community, territory is only one of the adjustments made between individuals of the same species in living together. Among some species of birds, for instance, each individual in a community usually has its own place in a despotic order. Challenge and conflict are continual, with a constant shifting of positions; the result is a peck order in which an individual maintains a position superior to some birds but subservient to others except, of course, for the bird at the top which is subservient to none. Once an individual loses a challenge from a bird beneath it on the ladder, it no longer has a position; it must make a challenge and eventually find a place lower down that it can defend. But the bird that has taken over the higher position has left a vacuum below it which is now filled by combat between the eligible birds farther down the ladder, including the dislocated bird. All of this can be seen by anyone observing the behavior of birds at a feeding station; out of a seemingly patternless confusion of birds, a social hierarchy is usually soon established, very precisely among birds of the same species and in a more general way among all the visitors to the feeding station.

Feeding, in fact, shows other evidences of social adjustments among birds. The mangrove coast of southern Florida is populated by a wide variety of herons, and sometimes as many as nine species feed together on the same shoal. The primary food of all of these heron species is fish, yet the birds have developed such a diverse repertoire of feeding techniques and behavioral responses that they rarely come into conflict with each other. The basic method of heron feeding, best exemplified by the green heron, is simply to take a position at the edge of a tide pool and wait motionless for a fish to pass by. The common egret is master of a variation of this method: instead of waiting for the prey, it stalks it by walking exceedingly slowly with its head extended and bill pointing downward. The great blue heron carries this method one step further: as it stalks it gives quick flicks of its wings, which startle potential prey into activity and makes them visible. The Louisiana heron incites its prey into movement by whirling, pirouetting or racing through the water and then stopping suddenly. The most elaborate method of all is used by the reddish egret, which first stirs up the water, then stops and forms a canopy with its extended wings under which the startled prey takes refuge in a false security.

Not only does each species of heron have its own feeding methods, but also the different species forage in different parts of the shoal. The very small green heron confines itself to the shallow water near the prop roots of the mangrove; the great white and great blue herons, the largest species found in this area, forage at the very tip of the shoal where the water is deepest, and the other species generally distribute themselves in depths that correspond to the length of their legs. The physical structure of each of the herons, combined with its behavioral methods of feeding and its preference for various portions of the shoal, all serve to reduce competition among the large number of species that inhabit this community. The available space and the food resources of the fish have been broken down into a number of compartments, each of which a particular heron species is best able to fill. The result is that all species benefit by sharing and making greater use of the habitat. If all species were to attempt to feed in the same manner in the same places, the inevitable result would be crowding, threats and fights, and thus a loss in the amount of time available for feeding.

The ability of living things to coexist in a community is only one of the factors characterizing it. Equally important is the tendency of the community to reproduce itself. One community succeeds another until a stage is reached where the whole, with all its various living organisms, is in approximate equilibrium with its environment. It may take decades or even thousands of years for this equilibrium to be achieved—but even then this balance is still not unchanging. The mature community is vulnerable to the slow processes of earth change, which is going on continually, as well as to sudden catastrophes. The New England hurricane of 1938, for example, swept through many square miles of primeval forest, disrupting its equilibrium and setting it far back to earlier stages of development; a similar effect will result from a landslide or a fire.

During each of the successive stages through which a community passes, there is change in most if not all of the organisms that make it up. New plants and animals appear. And their appearance brings about changes in the environment which actually serve to make living conditions less hospitable for the old inhabitants but more hospitable for the new ones. Thus a lichen can colonize bare rock; but once it has done so, it has created small amounts of soil in which mosses flourish, forcing out the lichens. The mosses in turn create even more soil and have water-holding ability; they make conditions favorable for small seed plants, with which the mosses can no longer compete. These, in turn, shelter the seedlings of shrubs and trees, which soon overtop them and deprive them of sunlight and root space. This process of continual development gradually slows down until a period of equilibrium is reached, known as the climax. The climax is distinguished by the fact that it reproduces itself: the conditions it creates are stable only for the offspring of its own kind.

THE succession of changes in a community can be seen very clearly on a sand dune. Lake Michigan furnishes some of the most interesting examples: its dunes have been intensively studied and many pioneer concepts in ecology were developed there. Along the shores of the lake, fresh sand is washed up by the waves onto the beach and blown into small dunes. These developing dunes are blown inland until they reach the shelter of an established dune or get beyond the full force of the wind or become anchored by vegetation. Thus, as one walks inland from the Lake Michigan shore, a sequence is seen of increasingly more-established stages. The lower beach, washed by summer storm waves, is devoid of vegetation or indeed of any permanent life whatever. The only living things that exist are the casualties of the drift, cast ashore by the waves to provide a meal for flesh flies and scavenger beetles, which in turn are preyed upon by other insects and by spotted sandpipers. A little farther inland is the strip of the middle beach that lies between the wet sands and the low dunes of the upper beach. Only the severe winter storms reach this far inland and it is here that the first pioneering plants appear, a scattered growth of annuals. Animal life makes a sparse appearance, with many of the same scavenger and predator forms present that invade the lower beach; but some of the organic matter cast high on the beach is by now mixed with the sands by termites and various burrowing beetles and has begun the creation of soil.

Shifting dunes form on the upper beach until they are covered by grasses and other vegetation. Their roots bind together the sand particles, and their leaves and stems serve as obstructions that slow down the movement of the blowing sand. After the sand has been stabilized for a while, shrubs encroach into the

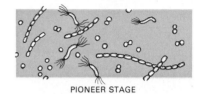

PIONEER STAGE

FLAGELLATE STAGE

PARAMECIUM STAGE

CLIMAX COMMUNITY

BUILDING COMMUNITIES

How a succession of species will form a community such as might be found in ponds can be shown in a simple infusion of hay and sterile water seeded with just a few drops of pond water. Bacteria and protozoans replace each other as dominant species (above), with each species altering the food supply and paving the way for its successor's rise even as it prepares its own demise. The end stage, or climax, is a state of balance in which green algae, rotifers, crustaceans and amoebas coexist with only scattered representatives from the earlier stages.

grasses and the first trees appear, usually eastern cottonwoods. Up to this point, the succession of life has been dominated largely by the shifting sands, but inland from the cottonwoods the invasion of new species depends on the development of more and more soil humus, which provides nutrients and water for trees to grow. And as the trees increase in number, size and diversity, they provide more shelter and food for a wider variety of animals. The cottonwood zone is followed farther inland by a dense forest of pines with a complex community of life. The pines, depositing their needles upon the sands, create soil deep enough for the next stage in the succession, the oaks and hickories, to take hold. Ultimately, the final stage of climax is reached with the growth of a mature forest of beeches and sugar maples under whose dense canopy only the shade-tolerant seedlings of its own kind can grow. This kind of forest remains essentially the same year after year, providing no catastrophes upset its equilibrium.

Something, however, usually does occur—and that is why any description of succession to a climax is probably an idealized and perhaps unrealistic one. Actually, the stages of succession at Lake Michigan—or elsewhere—do not proceed smoothly, but rather by a long series of lurches and setbacks. Strong winds may blow dunes so far inland that they engulf the established forests, leaving only denuded trunks of smothered trees. The so-called climax communities anywhere are so often subject to catastrophes of severe weather, lightning-caused fire, earthquakes and volcanoes that their state of equilibrium is at best a temporary one. In a forest with a large population of deer, severe weather conditions might destroy a climax it took centuries to create. Deep snows may so deprive the deer of their normal winter food that the starving animals will attack the bark of trees, often completely girdling the trunks so that the trees die. The sudden opening of the leaf canopy allows the forest floor to be flooded with sunlight, drying it out, killing many of its inhabitants or forcing them to leave. Rain, which formerly splattered harmlessly on the green roof of the forest, now can reach the soil surface and cause severe erosion. In fact, so transient is the equilibrium of the climax stage, that there is currently disagreement among ecologists as to whether climaxes actually exist as the textbooks describe them or whether they are not merely a convenient label.

In fact, when one examines a community, it is difficult to see in it the stability that is connoted by the popular idea of "the balance of nature." A rocky shore in the northern latitudes is periodically battered by storm waves and scraped clear of life by ice; it goes through constant cycles of being denuded and replenished, sometimes as often as every four years. Even the coral reef, one of the world's most stable communities, is subject to marked changes. Every long-term rise or fall in the level of the sea, every slow change in the crust of the earth itself can utterly destroy the corals upon which the whole superstructure of the life of the reef is erected. Rather than a single balance of nature, one should probably visualize a multitude of balances in the world of living things. These balances should not be depicted as the single scales balanced upon a fulcrum, but rather as a roomful of clocks of every size and description, with pendulums that vary in their swings from year to year and from moment to moment. Nevertheless, all of these clocks, unless seriously tampered with by the heavy hand of man or disaster, manage to keep approximately the same time, and their pendulums swing within fairly definite limits. Change rather than stability is the key to the understanding of the world of living things—and that is what makes this minor planet of an insignificant sun such a fascinating place to live.

SURF-LASHED OUTER REEFS OF THE CORNISH COAST ARE BLACK WITH MUSSELS, FIRMLY TETHERED TO THE CLEAN, ERODED ROCK SURFACES

A Wave-swept Home

On the rocky littoral, between high and low tide marks, the entire fabric of an ecological community and its problems of survival narrows down to a single wave-washed boulder or rock pool. There, periodically submerged and exposed to the sun and wind, plants and animals have adapted to a demanding existence by developing anchors and mooring lines, to hold their niche against the sea.

THE LITTORAL

The face of a sea cliff is zoned like a mountain-side. Luxuriant seaweed cover in the low tide zone harbors the greatest number of animal species; only a few colonize the barren, exposed peak.

THE "SEA SNAIL" is actually a small fish shaped like a garden slug. Relatively immobile, it fastens by a sucker on its chest to rocks covered with red seaweed and budding thong weed.

SPRING TIDES EXPOSE DEEP WATER KELP ON THE FRINGES OF THE LITTORAL.

Where the Tides Hold Sway

On the rocky south coast of Britain the tidal wave rolls in every 12 hours and 25 minutes. Less regular is the range of the tide: at any given point, it varies from day to day and week to week. At new and full moon, the "spring" tides pile up higher and drop lower than at intervening quarter moons, or "neap" tides; at these times the sun and moon are both aligned with the earth and their combined gravitational pull sweeps water onto the highest rock surfaces, otherwise barely touched by spray. From these almost terrestrial reaches down to the lowest levels, exposed for only a few minutes at a time, the littoral supports a variety of plants and animals including algae, lichens, and several species of periwinkles, acorn barnacles, marine limpets, mussels, sea snails, anemones, sponges, starfishes and tube-building bristle worms. Large brown seaweeds cling by hold-fasts in the low tide zone, where encrusting organisms spread over sheltered rock niches, filtering the ebb and flow of the sea for its gifts of plankton.

GOLDEN STAR TUNICATES stick in a jellylike sheet to the undersurface of a rock, straining their own sea water, but water and waste are expelled through the center of each cluster.

BREAD CRUMB SPONGE, reinforced with particles of lime, sweeps water through its walls by the action of millions of microscopic cells, and releases it through large perforations.

TS LONG STEMS INTERMIXED WITH THE LACY BLADES OF SERRATED WRACK, A BROWN SEAWEED WHICH COVERS THE REST OF THE LOW TIDE ZONE

RED BEADLET SEA ANEMONES CLING TO THE BOTTOM OF A ROCK POOL BY A FLEXIBLE BASAL COLUMN, BUT THE SPIRALED TOP SHELL AND CONICA

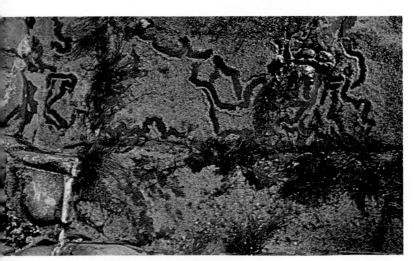

HIEROGLYPHICS IN THE SAND are etched by top shells, which move about and graze on minute algae and diatoms under tidal cover. Their broad adhesive feet leave a tangle of trails.

LIMPET SCARS, carved by the 70-pounds-per-square-inch pull of the foot and its corrosive secretion, fit their owners' shells perfectly. They usually return to the same scar after feeding.

48

LIMPET HANG ON WITH A FOOT ALMOST AS LARGE AS THEIR SHELLS

MUSSELS SECRETE THREADS like guy ropes by which they cling to rocks and each other. Packing protects some from predatory dog whelks, but if the bottom layer dies, all fall off.

THE MID-TIDE ZONE

Plants and animals receive from 15 to 55 per cent exposure to sun, wind and rain at the mid-tide level, which is characterized by a broad band of knotted wrack, barnacles and other organisms.

Between Two Worlds

Mid-tide is the most restless level on the rocky shore, a continual compromise between wet and dry, hot and cold, a seaborne and a stationary existence. Knotted wrack, the prevailing variety of seaweed, grows long, stringy fronds which are buoyed up by numerous large vesicles filled with the oxygen-rich gas produced by the plants. Here the barnacles, bivalve mollusks and snails develop higher shells with thicker domes because of frequent desiccation and contraction, and gill openings become smaller to prevent the rapid evaporation of water. Some species manufacture a mucus which seals in moisture, and all are more capable of tolerating higher temperatures, water loss and the resulting concentrations of salt in the body fluids.

The intertidal rock pool at this level provides a small asylum to which salt-water organisms may retreat when the tides are out. But even in its calm depths there are dangers, especially at higher levels. Rain may dilute the pool, or sun may evaporate it so that salt actually crystallizes around its edges. Sometimes the temperature of the water exceeds 105°F., lethal even for the extremely adaptable mussels. Dense growths of algae in the bottom produce so much oxygen in sunlight that streams of bubbles rise to the surface, yet at night there may be an oxygen deficit. With the sudden return of the tide there is a complete interchange with sea water, restoring the conditions for feeding and, in the spring of the year, for recolonizing the zones on the shore.

THE HIGH TIDE ZONE
Brown seaweeds adapted for 60 to 90 per cent exposure to the air afford the last plant cover for the fauna of the littoral. Above are encampments of barnacles and almost terrestrial periwinkles.

The Last Frontier

Pioneering barnacles and periwinkles ordinarily cover the upper littoral. Their populations are regularly replenished by the young, which float in from the sea on the spring flood tides, often attaching themselves near established groups of adults. Occasionally barnacles settle where they will not be able to mature when the tide drops. Unable to maneuver down into a wetter environment, they die. Periwinkles, however, are mobile creatures. Impelled by a complex gravity-overcoming mechanism to move up the beach, each species advances as far as it can without excessive drying, the rough periwinkle stopping at the limits of the seaweed and the small periwinkle going on to reach the high spring tide mark.

SHELTERING IN HIGH CREVICES, small periwinkles glue their shells to rock with mucus, pull in a retractable foot, and then close their spiral homes with a horny plate, the operculum.

SPANGLED WITH GOLD, leaves of channeled wrack near the high water mark grow so dry between tides that they crumble at a touch. This seaweed is covered 60 minutes every 12 hours.

TWO VIEWS OF HONEYCOMB WORMS show their adaptations for living in tubes. Tentacles on the front feet trap food, and the coiled abdomen discharges wastes through the entrance. Gills appear as a dark fringe along the smaller worm's back.

The Surf-beaten Belt

Sheltered cliffs, overgrown with seaweeds, harbor a great variety of marine animals, but only a few of these—including barnacles, mussels, dog whelks, beadlet anemones and tube-building worms—persist on the rocks facing the sea, worn smooth by breakers. Under each successive wave, the plumes and cirri of the filter-feeders sweep and beat incessantly, and the predators mobilize tentacles and drills to capture and devour their prey. The niches they occupy at low tide are sometimes as special as the crevices filled by the periwinkles in the high tide zone. The honeycomb worm, for example, always forms its colonies where the rocky shore has eroded and the waves are rough enough to carry the sand to the builders but will not sweep them out to sea.

CLUSTERS OF TUBES are erected by honeycomb worms where eroded shore meets sandy bottom. As the worms grow, they lengthen their tunnels by gluing more sand to the openings.

WITHDRAWN AT EBB TIDE, these honeycomb worms, magnified six times, have closed their tubes with plated and spiked feet to protect their soft bodies from sun, wind and enemies.

3

Why Living Things Are Where They Are

I AM earth's native: no rearranging it!'' warned Robert Browning. But man has
not heeded the poet's wise advice. In these days of so-called "Colombian"
coffee, "Washington" apples and "Kentucky" bluegrass, one is apt to lose
sight of the fact that coffee, apples and bluegrass never grew in the New World
until brought across the Atlantic by man. Few people except botanists realize
how indebted the North American meadows, pastures and much of the cultivated landscape are to the Old World. Everywhere, in fact, that man now re-
sides on the globe, he is surrounded by transported vegetation, although these
alien plants are so abundant as weeds or as cultivated crops that most people
take them for natives.

In the absence of man, and sometimes despite his intrusion, all living things
are united in delicate interdependence with other living things. Various mechanisms isolate one species from another; they are among the most important attributes a species possesses, for they are the very criteria of what makes a species.
They prevent interbreeding and thus preserve the species as a unique plant or
animal. But, on the other hand, every living thing has a capacity to spread, and
there is at least one dispersal stage in its life cycle. This tendency to spread is

ISOLATION—
BY SONG AND DISPLAY

Closely related species that look alike are often kept from hybridizing by differences in mating behavior. Ritual calls and postures, as in the black-headed gull (below) and the little gull (opposite), are some of the ways in which species occupying the same range recognize each other and thus can isolate themselves.

LONG-CALL POSTURE

FORWARD POSTURE

FACING-AWAY POSTURE

Swaggering in the "long-call" position, the male black-headed gull (above) gives out a cry peculiar to its species alone. When a female approaches, it suddenly stares straight ahead. If the female is also a black-headed gull, she imitates his posture. In the last stance, both jerk upright and face away from each other.

balanced by the ecological barriers of mountains and seas and by internal barriers such as the physiology and psychology of the organism itself.

Trees are typical examples of this double quality of unity and isolation. Most kinds of forest trees have formed a partnership with certain soil fungi which grow into and upon their roots, markedly increasing their efficiency in absorbing nutrients. But the partnership imposes barriers, too—trees will not grow where the fungi are lacking. During the 1930s, when great windbreaks were planted in the Great Plains grasslands, many of the new trees did not thrive until essential fungi were artificially introduced into the soil in which the seedlings were being grown.

ONE can easily visualize the barriers to the distribution of plants rooted to the ground, and the limitations imposed upon small mammals which are incapable of long treks. But what about birds? Many of them have the muscle to make nonstop ocean-spanning flights and they have been free to fly wherever they pleased for the approximately 150 million years that they have possessed wings. Yet, most kinds of birds inhabit invisible cages, with even some migratory species restricted to relatively narrow corridors on their long flights. People correctly associate ptarmigans with the tundra, birds of paradise with the islands of Melanesia, hummingbirds with the New World. One of the most widespread birds in the world is the marsh hawk, which is not finicky about its food and is highly adaptable; yet even this bird is found only in certain kinds of wet woodlands. South America is populated by some 300 different kinds of hummingbirds, but Africa, with many similar environments, does not have a single hummingbird—although hummingbirds possess strong powers of flight. Finches, found even on remote oceanic islands, do not inhabit Australia; the Ipswich sparrow nests only on Sable Island, Nova Scotia; the Laysan teal inhabits perhaps the tiniest range of all birds, the shores of a marshy lagoon about two miles square on a small Hawaiian island. English sparrows and barn owls are among the few exceptions to this curious limitation to the distribution of birds: through their association with man, they have been able to spread widely.

Some of the reasons for birds being where they are despite their strong powers of flight are obvious. Large continental land masses can prevent the spread of sea birds, and ocean barriers may be insurmountable obstacles to land birds. When the Andes Mountains of South America rose in comparatively recent geological times, they split apart populations of birds in Colombia from those in Ecuador; today the descendants of those birds occupy the opposite sides of the mountain range and eventually may evolve into different races or perhaps even different species. That is already beginning to happen in the case of one ornate bird, the cock-of-the-rock, which is today represented by different subspecies on the Pacific and the Amazonian sides of the Andes.

But there is also a more subtle interplay of many other ecological factors that make for isolation. The brown pelican of the Caribbean is a sea bird that does not venture far from shore. Its feeding method—sighting fish from the air and then diving for them—restricts it to areas of clear water. The muddy outpouring from the mouth of the Amazon River into the Atlantic Ocean makes it impossible for the pelican to feed in that area and thus puts a southerly limit on its distribution. However, it has been predicted that if the pelicans ever did surmount this barrier, they would proliferate south of Brazil.

The ocean can present a barrier even to a sea bird, for there are warm-water species of birds and cold-water species. The royal tern is a widespread warm-water bird. On the Atlantic Coast of the New World its range extends from around Virginia southward to Argentina, spanning about 80 degrees of latitude. The warming effect of the Gulf Stream flowing northward allows it to extend its range in that direction, while the southward-flowing Brazil Current provides favorable conditions in the South Atlantic. But conditions are different on the Pacific Coast. There the cold California and Peru currents restrict the tern's range to only 30 degrees of latitude between southern California and Ecuador. Even fog may be an important climatic factor in limiting a species. Chicks of the widespread Arctic terns hatched in the Bay of Fundy have been found to gain weight on clear days, but lose weight on foggy days when the parent birds cannot find food. The fact that fogs are particularly frequent in places like the Bering Sea probably accounts for the absence of this species as a breeding bird there.

In addition to barriers of mountains, of sea, of climate, of lack of food plants and associated animals and plants, there may be purely psychological barriers that isolate species. Some land birds are extremely capable fliers but are isolated by their reluctance to fly across comparatively narrow water gaps: such common South and Central American birds as toucans, ovenbirds, puffbirds and manakins have not populated any of the nearby islands of the West Indies, and several other species have reached only one or two of them. An extreme case is that of the barbets, which have become isolated from each other by the broad tributaries of the Amazon basin and have developed into several races. The white-eye, a songbird of the central Solomon Islands in the Pacific, refuses to fly a few miles to nearby islands—even though its flying equipment is essentially the same as that of a close relative that does not possess this inhibition and bridged the thousand-mile gap between Tasmania and New Zealand.

A LONG with the psychological factors that isolate animals, there may be other mechanisms at work. Two closely related species of moths, for example, that are fully capable of interbreeding and producing hybrid offspring, do not do so under natural conditions because the adults emerge from their cocoons at different seasons of the year and thus the sexes can never meet. Laboratory manipulation of their life cycles, however, has delayed the emergence of one species, with the result that under these artificial conditions they interbreed. An unusual example of an isolating mechanism is the case of two races of the same species of salmon, the so-called steelhead and rainbow trout—they spawn at the same time and on the same grounds in the waters of British Columbia, but the steelhead migrates to and from the ocean while the rainbow never leaves fresh water. Differences in migratory behavior may possibly bring about the eventual division of this single species, with two races now fully capable of interbreeding, into two distinct species.

It is on islands that one can witness the forces of isolation at work in the most direct way—as well as the forces of invasion since the coming of modern man. The problems of life on islands are not always typical of those encountered in other habitats; nevertheless, islands show with clarity the ecological relationships of living things and why living things are where they are. When Captain Cook anchored off Easter Island in 1774, he noted in his journal: "Nature has been exceedingly sparing of her favours to this spot." The fact that nature had got there at all seems rather miraculous, since South America is 2,000 miles distant and the nearest vegetated Pacific island is a thousand miles away. Before the coming of European man, Easter Island possessed fewer than 50 species

LONG-CALL POSTURE

VERTICAL POSTURE

UPRIGHT POSTURE

Although man may easily confuse the little gull (above) with the black-headed gull (opposite), the two birds under natural conditions seldom confuse each other. The little gull greets the female with a vertical posture, then both demurely tilt heads. These rituals, repeated several times, will usually end in mating.

of flowering plants, ferns and mosses; there were only five kinds of animals living on the island, four of them insects and the fifth a land snail. Many of the other volcanic islands and tiny coral atolls that dot the Pacific Ocean like the Milky Way were similarly impoverished, with the exception of the Hawaiian Islands, which possessed a rich native flora and abundant bird life. Surrounded by extensive sea barriers and never connected to any of the distant continents, these truly oceanic islands are in strong contrast to the continental islands—notably the British Isles, Japan and many of the islands of Indonesia—which were connected to the continents in the past by land bridges.

Land mammals are nearly always absent on oceanic islands. Even islands as large as New Zealand's possess no native land mammals except bats, the only mammals which have the power of flight. Fresh-water animals have had especial difficulty in reaching islands surrounded by barriers of sea water, and so most oceanic islands completely lack, or are impoverished of, amphibians, aquatic insects and fresh-water fishes. However, when species do manage to reach the remote islands, there often is a tremendous degree of diversification by a single species into numerous species that fill a wide variety of ecological niches. On the oceanic islands of Hawaii an array of organisms developed that once marked this as one of the most distinct communities in the world. The extreme isolation of the islands in mid-Pacific permitted the arrival of only a few kinds of immigrants, but these few kinds diversified widely. This has been easier in the Hawaiian Islands because of their division into a few relatively large land masses, in addition to many satellite islands, reefs and shoals. Thus an animal might evolve into half a dozen species on as many different islands, whereas there would have been only a single, wide-ranging species if the land area had been one continuous mass. Once a few individuals have been carried by chance across an oceanic barrier to an island and are thus isolated from their parent stock, certain differences begin to arise almost immediately in the isolated animals. Were further invasions to be made from the parent stock, then these new mutations would be overwhelmed. But that has not happened on Hawaii because of its extreme isolation and the improbability of frequent over-water dispersal. There new mutants have arisen and further diverged into additional species as they came under the influence of local ecological conditions on each of the islands.

Hawaii has indeed produced some amazing examples of adaptive radiation that have filled many niches. The nymphs of damsel flies around the world, for instance, are commonly aquatic, yet on Hawaii one species has been found that has adapted to life on land, crawling about in the ground litter in search of prey. Groups of bees, which in other places in the world are nonparasitic, on Hawaii have developed parasitic species. Relatives of the delicate lacewings have given rise to flightless insect monsters encased in armorlike wings.

A particularly remarkable evolutionary diversification into food-habit types on the Hawaiian Islands is seen in the honey creepers, which have evolved to fill ecological gaps left vacant by the absence of other kinds of birds. On the islands today there are some 40 subspecies, or races, of honey creepers, all of which evolved from a single species of bird, probably a warbler or a tanager, that managed to cross the 2,000 miles of ocean from North America.

Isolation on oceanic islands has had numerous other effects upon living things that can be clearly seen. Forms of life that have become extinct on continents may persist on a remote island. For example, there is a small snail that lingers in the Azores, although its only known relatives died out during the Tertiary period. Certain forms of life, particularly birds, flourish on islands due to the scarcity or absence of mammalian predators. At the western end of the Malay Archipelago, where mammals are present, pigeons are scarce; but as one proceeds eastward through the Melanesian islands, where the mammals steadily decline, the pigeons increase markedly and reach their most striking abundance in the specks of Polynesian islands, where no native mammals are present at all.

Another special condition of islands is the clear-cut limit to their size. On many of them, there is simply not much living space and this affects the size of the animals that do live there. A single plant may form a microhabitat for an insect, but a grazing animal such as a deer may require tens of acres of forest to find enough food and to live freely; and a carnivore which must roam far in search of prey needs much more. Not only does the individual animal require space, but there also must be enough space for a population sufficiently large to ensure reproduction. Where area and numerical strength are at a minimum, a species either dies out or adapts by becoming smaller. The island of Bali, about 2,500 square miles in area, seems to be the smallest Asiatic island that can support a population of tigers.

SMALL islands, furthermore, usually have small mammals: island races of horses are usually dwarfed, such as those on the Shetland Islands, Iceland and the Japanese Islands. Deer, too, become dwarfed on islands, as seen in the key deer of Florida and the sika deer of Japan. The gray fox of Catalina Island, off the coast of southern California, does not reach the same size as the same species living on the mainland. On the other hand, large reptiles may be found on islands, since some of these relicts from the Age of Reptiles have been able to survive only there. The largest living turtles inhabit the Galápagos Islands off Ecuador, and the largest living lizard, the Komodo "dragon," is confined to islands in the Dutch East Indies.

A high-speed picture of how islands are populated was provided by a unique and dramatic event in 1883, when the violent explosion of a volcano tore apart the island of Krakatoa, near Java in the East Indies. The blast was equal to that of a 10,000-megaton H-bomb, and all that was left of the island after six cubic miles of rock were blown into the air was a peak completely coated with pumice and ashes. Every trace of life must have been obliterated, although it has been debated that possibly a few roots, spores of fungi or soil organisms survived in protected crevices. The sterilized island soon became for biologists an outdoor laboratory for the study of how plants and animals become distributed over the earth. Repopulation was expected to take place rapidly, for the nearest populated island was only 25 miles away (another island, a mere 12 miles distant, had been similarly sterilized by the explosion).

That is indeed what happened. Nine months after the eruption, a botanist who visited the island could find only a single species of life, a lonely spider spinning a web to snare a nonexistent prey. But only three years after the eruption, conditions had changed markedly: 11 species of ferns and 15 of flowering plants had returned. An additional 10 years found the scars of the explosion covered over by a layer of green growth. Young coconut trees grew along the shore; there was a scattering of wild sugar cane, and even four species of orchids. A quarter century after the eruption, 263 species of animals had managed to make their way to the island—mostly insects, but also 16 kinds of birds, two kinds of reptiles and four species of land snails. Less than a half century after the explosion, the whole island was again covered with a dense forest, although

HOW PLANTS TRAVEL

Seeds, spores and fruits carried by birds and other animals, by wind and by ocean currents were the initial colonizers of the plant world on the island of Krakatoa after a volcanic explosion denuded it in

PEMPHIS ACIDULA

1883. Birds, insects and some swimming animals—even man—accounted for about eight per cent of the transport for seeds that grew into Krakatoa's new plant cover. The seed case of one typical plant, the herb seen above, is adapted to hook on or stick tight to a bird's

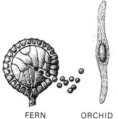

FERN   ORCHID   REED

feathers. Winds accounted for another 32 per cent of Krakatoa's colonizers. Some, like the spores of ferns, are so light that the wind carries them hundreds of miles. Others are kept in the air by tiny parachutes, wings, bristles and

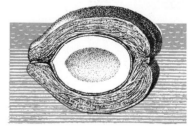

COCONUT

tufts. The remaining 60 per cent of the island's plants drifted ashore. Largest of these, the coconut is well fitted for a watery sojourn. It has a hard shell, a light, fibrous husk to help it float, and a coat of wax to prevent water seepage.

still young and low-growing. There were also now 47 species of vertebrates, mostly birds and bats, but also two kinds of rats.

How did this sudden repopulation take place? The lightweight seeds of grasses and orchids and the spores of ferns are easily carried by the wind. The heavy seeds of the coconut palm, which are the coconuts themselves, must have arrived by sea. Other kinds of plants with large seeds, such as figs and papayas, must have been brought to Krakatoa by birds, which ate their fleshy fruit but carried the seeds in their digestive tracts. Animals arrived on the wing or on floating debris. Life on Krakatoa now seems abundant, but it has by no means reached an equilibrium. Not all of the native flora and fauna has returned and the relationships between the species are not yet in balance. Rats, for example, in some years may overrun the vegetation, while in other years scarcely a rat can be found.

Krakatoa was only 25 miles distant from an abounding source of life, but suppose it had been thousands of miles away from the nearest island? In that case, it might well have been thousands of years before a plant cover was formed. Even thousands of years is probably too conservative a time span. Studies of the distribution of plants on Java and Sumatra reveal that several million years have not been enough time for the complete filling of all available ecological niches. The volcanoes on these islands are not more than a few million years old; they are so high that lowland tropical plants cannot grow on them. Thus their peaks actually represent ecological islands. However, not all of the volcanoes have growing on them all of the different kinds of plants that their climate and soil will allow. One plant, the proliferous primrose, which originated in the Himalayas and skipped from volcano to volcano across southeast Asia, is now found on a few volcanoes in Sumatra, about 1,500 miles away. But the plant grows on only three volcanoes, some 500 miles farther eastward in Java—although conditions are suitable for it on 17 others in the general vicinity.

I n the same way that remote islands allow one to appreciate more fully the building forces of life at work, they also offer dramatic instances of the effects of sudden invasion by alien plants and animals. The primitive animals that have endured on islands, and those that have lost their means of protection through the absence of enemies, are vulnerable to destruction by an alien. Wild dogs and cats, house rats and house mice, and other mammals which arrived with the first ships to reach these islands, have all been immediately destructive on islands which previously lacked predaceous mammals. Lord Howe Island, off the east coast of Australia, had a remarkable bird population until 1918, when rats from a wrecked ship swarmed ashore. Within two years the island's birds had been destroyed. Even the tiny Mascarens Islands in the Indian Ocean have witnessed the extinction in recent years of 36 kinds of animals. These extinctions and depredations are due usually to the sudden ascendancy of one or a few forms of life, usually alien, that rip apart the fabric of life. They cause what are known as "ecological explosions"—the sudden bursting out from control of a plant or animal previously held in restraint by a physical barrier or by other living things. Ecological explosions occur not only on islands—although they are often most dramatically seen there—but anywhere that life is present: the virtual annihilation of the American chestnut tree was due to a fungus blight imported into the New York City area by plants brought over from Asia.

The havoc man has played in breaking down the barriers of life by introducing foreign forms is seen in its extreme in New Zealand, where a primeval para-

ABUNDANT ■
NUMEROUS ▦
SPARSE ▢

Lake Superior
1946
Soo Locks
St. Lawrence River
Lake Huron
Lake Ontario
1936
1937
Lake Michigan
1921
Lake Erie
Welland Canal

LANDLOCKED LAMPREY

The sea lamprey, which enters fresh water to spawn, has long shown its ability to adapt entirely to this environment. Thus its passage into the upper Great Lakes had been a possibility since 1829, when the Welland Canal was constructed around Niagara Falls, but this did not actually happen until the canal was deepened during the period between 1913 and 1918. Lake Erie was evidently too warm to encourage the lamprey's development, but in the succeeding years they gradually penetrated Lake Huron, Lake Michigan and finally Lake Superior. In those chill waters they multiplied and in the last two decades made devastating inroads on fish populations, especially lake trout.

dise was modified almost to the point of no return. Much of New Zealand is still spectacularly beautiful, but to the eye of the ecologist, seeking remnants of unique and vanished glory, many parts of it appear like a once-lovely countryside ravished by the bulldozer and landscape developer. Like other parts of the earth, New Zealand was subjected to natural changes that took place even without the hand of man: climatic cycles, glaciation, the gradual alteration in the communities of plants and animals. During the 400 years in which the Maoris, a Polynesian people, occupied the islands before the first visit of Captain Cook in 1769, they had already altered the face of the land. However, their influence was not disastrous. They introduced the inoffensive Polynesian rat and an unaggressive breed of dog, neither of which was predaceous upon the native fauna.

THE real damage began when European man arrived with his own brands of rats and dogs. In his second visit to New Zealand in 1773, and again in 1777, Captain Cook introduced the sheep, goat, pig, fowl, potato, cabbage, turnip and other aliens; visits by other explorers and whalers stocked the islands with still more alien plants and animals. It was a general practice at that time for ships to bring animals with them, which they liberated on many islands that seemed capable of supporting them. The incentives were a future food supply of fresh meat and a well-intentioned attempt to benefit the natives. Later, European birds such as the blackbird and the song thrush were introduced, and so were plants such as the blackberry and the brier rose. This was a double-barrelled error, for these birds have largely been responsible for the enormous spread of these almost-ineradicable plants. Rabbits became a serious problem by 1870; to control them, additional introductions of carnivorous mammals had to be made, such as weasels and ferrets. The result has been that both the carnivores and the rabbits remain abundant.

Introduction of alien forms of life accelerated in the last century when New Zealanders tried to reproduce the most cherished features of their European home and make this South Sea island group an imitation England. They brought in some 130 bird species, of which about 30 became established. Mammals were brought in: moose, elk, white-tailed and mule deer from North America; red deer and fallow deer from Europe; the sambar, rusa and sika deer, and wild sheep from Asia. A gift of some chamois by the Emperor Franz Josef resulted in a population of these mammals in New Zealand probably as great as in their native European Alps. Of the 48 introduced mammals, 25 have gone wild, including descendants of such domestic animals as pigs, horses, sheep, goats and cats. The populations of horned grazing animals have grown to immense size. These grazers, plus the wild goats and pigs, are destroying forests which developed through untold ages. Eating them from the top down is the worst pest in New Zealand today, the Australian opossum, or phalanger, introduced as a potential fur resource in 1858. So abundant are these little marsupials that even electric-power poles have to be sheathed with bands of iron to prevent the animals from climbing them and short-circuiting the wires.

As for plants, somewhere between 400 and 600 species have been introduced into New Zealand, although not all of them were immediately successful in disrupting the native vegetation. Many, however, flourished in nightmare fashion. The European watercress, which attains only a modest size in its native habitat, develops stems as thick as a man's wrist in New Zealand; it grows 14 feet in length and chokes the channels of rivers. More than half of the original New Zealand forest has been converted into grassland, much of it worthless. Erosion

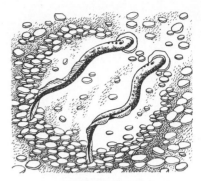

SPAWNING ADULTS

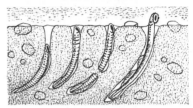

GROWING LARVAE

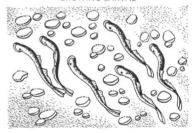

MIGRATORY YOUNG

PARASITIC ADULTS

BREAKING A LIFE CYCLE

In decades of unremitting labor, scientists working to get the Great Lakes lampreys under control learned that the only truly vulnerable part of their life cycles was the larval stage. Traps and even electrical barriers to kill migrating young or adults at the spawning grounds proved ineffectual, but by 1958 a specific poison had been found which kills the larvae during their five-year growth period in the bottom mud. With this, hope came at last of restoring the rich fisheries.

has been rampant; rivers that once were navigable channels between wooded banks are now scattered runnels that in flood season become muddy torrents.

New Zealand has been the scene not of a single ecological explosion, but of burst after burst of destruction. The same sort of thing is happening all over the globe—on islands and continents, in rivers and lakes, on mountains and deserts, even in the depths of the sea. With each decade, Wallace's realms are having less significance. Animals that were never able to penetrate foreign realms have been helped over the barriers by man and have spread rapidly. For example, the gray squirrel was introduced from North America into several places in the British Isles between 1830 and 1890. By 1930, due to intentional releases and the escape of pet animals, the squirrel was present in at least 33 separate centers, with a total area of some 1,400 square miles. In one area, the squirrel spread from 274 locations to 708 in about seven years. Even more of an explosion into a new realm resulted from the release of five muskrats, once found exclusively in the Nearctic realm, by a landowner in Czechoslovakia in 1905; this introduction has been followed by others for fur breeding. Today many millions of muskrats inhabit Europe; introductions into the Soviet Union have allowed its spread through the great river systems of Siberia and northern Russia. Even little Finland has an annual catch that ranges between 100,000 and 240,000 animals. The British Isles were able to eradicate the few thousand muskrats that became established there—but to do so, they paid a high price in the sacrifice of native animals caught in the traps set for the capture of muskrats. Less than a thousand muskrats were killed in two rivers in Scotland, but 5,783 native mammals and birds were also caught in the muskrat traps.

The list of animals that have managed to invade foreign realms is a long one and it includes some of the most familiar figures in the landscape. The starling is a Eurasian bird that was intentionally liberated in Central Park, New York City, in 1891; today it abounds from coast-to-coast and from Alaska to northern Mexico. The sea lamprey, a primitive fish that fastens itself with a sucking disk onto other fishes and feeds on their blood and body fluids, entered Lake Erie through the Welland Canal around 1918, spread from there into the other lakes and ruined the once-prosperous Great Lakes trout fisheries in just a few decades. The gypsy moth, the object of federal and state eradication campaigns now estimated to cost a total of two million dollars annually, is a European insect that escaped from the cage of a Frenchman in Massachusetts who was trying to cross it with the silkworm. In fact, many of our most destructive insect pests are not native, but rather foreign invaders which have left their natural parasites, predators and other controls behind them.

MAN today inhabits a planet on which a multitude of organisms from all parts of the world are being mingled. Animals and plants are on the move. A disease from Brazil, myxomatosis, has nearly obliterated the rabbits of Australia, Britain and western Europe. In recent years the Colorado potato beetle has arrived in Europe and is causing severe losses. Everywhere it seems that vast changes are taking place in the natural balances of the world's inhabitants. A hundred years of increasingly faster transportation has multiplied the bombardment of every realm by foreign species. Today man is accelerating what were once gradual changes in the communities of living things that took place over millions of years. "We must make no mistake," states Dr. Charles Elton, a leading ecologist. "We are seeing one of the great historical convulsions in the world's fauna and flora."

NOW RECOLONIZING THE LAVA OUTFLOW OF NYAMLAGIRA VOLCANO IN THE CONGO, THESE FERNS FIRST ARRIVED AS WINDBORNE SPORES

Balance and Explosion

The almost frightening mobility latent in many plants and animals is seldom evident in the normal life of a balanced community. But if disaster strikes—a volcanic explosion or some man-induced invasion of a new species—the vitality which long ago enabled these diverse living things to colonize the earth immediately comes into play, with results often as startling as they are irreversible.

63

KRAKATOA: WHERE LIFE BEGAN AGAIN

When the top blew off the volcanic island of Krakatoa near Java one summer morning in 1883, it brought the end, for all practical purposes, of that particular little world. Nothing survived the apocalyptic explosion—not a plant, not an animal, not a seed, not a spore. When the dust had settled and the lava cooled, the island was as sterile as might have been the primeval rock from which the earth was formed, eons ago.

To scientists, this huge natural catastrophe presented an unexampled opportunity. How long would it be before Krakatoa became a living community again? What would be the first forms of life to take hold and how would they develop? The answers, in many respects surprising, are shown on these pages.

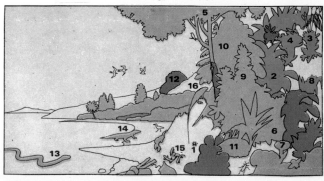

THE RECOLONIZATION OF KRAKATOA took place by sea and by air, with most of the colonists coming from Java and Sumatra, some 25 miles away. In this painting, the numbers identifying different species are color-coded to show how various animals and plants arrived—green if by sea, purple if bird-borne, blue if wafted on the wind. First to be seen on the island was a spider (1), found in its web nine months after the eruption. Airborne algae soon spread blue-green growths that formed a base on which the microscopic spores of mosses and ferns (2), and lightweight seeds of such flowering plants as

Emilia (3) and Wedelia (4), could germinate. Seaborne seeds of the Calophyllum tree (5) floated ashore and took root, and those of the Tournefortia shrub (6) and Ipomoea (7) were carried there on debris. As a more hospitable soil was formed, less hardy plants established themselves. By 1896 seeds of the wild sugar cane, dropped by the wind, had formed extensive stands, and even the minute sporelike seeds of delicate orchids (8) were able to find a suitable loam. Seeds of the tropical strand-forest trees, the Barringtonia (9) and Casuarina (10), as well as coconuts (11), were tossed above the tidemark and began to grow. Scavenging birds and insects were probably early visitors, and others settled when their requisite plant associates were present. The birds brought the seeds of figs (12) and other plants in their digestive tracts. Other seeds and minute animals clung to their feathers and feet. Except for such strong swimmers as the python (13) and monitor (14), most of the reptiles—geckos (15), Calotes (16) and skinks—must have reached the island, either alive or as eggs, on floating debris. Within 50 years, recovery was assured, with a thick young forest and over 1,200 species of animals established.

65

A Tree That Builds Up Land

In the salt or brackish waters of tropical and sub-tropical seacoasts, the red mangrove shows an ability not only to survive and colonize an environment impossible for most other trees, but even to create new land. A tangle of roots and trunks that seems at first undecipherable, a mangrove forest on closer examination sorts itself out into a meaningful structure that actually traps flotsam of all kinds in the shallow waters where it grows, gradually forming solid ground from the decaying mass. The origin of a mangrove forest can be a single seedling which, before separating from the parent tree, develops a long root (*right*). When it falls, the seedling is almost a finished young plant: it may strike into mud below and take hold there, or it may float off on the tide to travel a thousand miles. Wherever it does finally lodge, it establishes itself quickly—as on the sand bar shown below—and grows with great rapidity, to reproduce itself within five years.

A TANGLE OF MANGROVES slowly extends its range as new seedlings (*foreground*) root on the bottom. Behind the roots and trunks of older trees soil has formed from debris.

ROOT-CARRYING SEEDLINGS at various stages of development hang from a red mangrove. Roots may grow 12 inches long and a half inch in diameter at the tip before dropping.

ONCE ROOTED, THE MANGROVE SEEDLINGS HAVE BEEN OBSERVED TO GROW AN INCH AN HOUR, AND BEAR FRUIT WHEN FOUR FEET HIGH

THE HELMETED CHAMELEON is one of a huge variety of this reptile family in Madagascar. Both the smallest (1½ inches) and the largest (over two feet) live there, 40 species in all.

80 Million Years Alone

Supposing that a group of animals—a variety of species established in the same environment—were physically isolated by some natural catastrophe from the rest of the world: would they evolve in their own fashion, to be discovered, perhaps, ages later as living relics of the past? Science fiction has toyed with this question; ecologists deal with it realistically, on islands. Madagascar, for example, 250 miles off the east coast of Africa, has been cut off from that continent for perhaps 80 million years. Since that long-ago time the island has acted as a refuge for forms of life that have become rare or extinct elsewhere. Of its plant life, for instance, 80 per cent is unique to the island, found nowhere

THE FRILLED GECKO of Madagascar is probably the most primitive member of this worldwide family. It does not even cast a shadow because its tattered skin melts into the tree bark on which it rests.

THE SPINY TENREC is one of a family of insect-eating mammals believed to be among the most primitive known. Its nearest kin are the two-foot solenodons of the West Indies.

THE SIFAKA, most monkeylike of the Madagascan lemurs, here clings to one of the island's unique plants, the branchless *Didierea*, which resembles a cactus but is completely unrelated.

else. Chameleons originated there *(opposite page)*, and Madagascar still has half of all the species known worldwide. There are also 46 genera of birds that occur nowhere else. Particularly interesting are Madagascar's lemurs, primates which elsewhere were unable to compete with their cousins, the monkeys, and so died out. Generally small in size and with considerably less developed brains than the monkeys, the lemurs throve in the isolation of their island and today their many species lead both diurnal and nocturnal lives and fill a wide variety of niches. Superstitious native tribes helped them to survive by putting the *fady*, or tabu, on them because they believed they once had been men.

THE RUFFED LEMUR can match a freshly clipped poodle in fancy dress, with its white collar, cuffs and sash. One of the handsomest of the species, it is a gentle herbivore and said to make a good pet.

The Dangerous Aliens

Quite another matter from evolution in isolation, as on an island, is the explosive growth of a species introduced into an alien but favorable environment in which normal controls, such as predators, are lacking. Australia has been experiencing the consequences of this for more than a century, ever since a colony of European wild rabbits was released there as an easy source of food and pelts. With no competition, the rabbits spread with such phenomenal rapidity—up to 70 miles per year—that they soon became a serious threat to the country's vast sheep- and cattle-grazing lands. Nothing could keep them in check, until, after World War II, the virus disease myxomatosis was introduced. It swept the rabbits like a scourge, with almost 100 per cent fatalities at first—but lately its effects seem to be waning, possibly because a disease-resistant strain is evolving.

BIOLOGICAL WARFARE is Australia's ultimate weapon to keep the rabbits in check. Here government wildlife researchers study the effects of myxomatosis on experimental animals.

A RABBIT-PROOF FENCE offers a graphic demonstration of the destructive ability of the Australian rabbit hordes. On the left, everything has been eaten except large trees and a few shrubs, reducing the land to a virtual desert. On the other side of the fence, the natural vegetation—lush by comparison —shows what could be available for sheep and cattle herds.

ARGENTINE COYPUS, the muskratlike animals which yield valuable nutria pelts, crowd a breeding pen in Buenos Aires. Brought to England and the United States, they became a major pest when a few escaped and multiplied rapidly because they found no natural enemies. Their burrowing activities are particularly damaging to dams, canals and drainage ditches.

IN THE CONGO, water hyacinths imported for their beauty now are a major threat to transportation in this struggling nation. Sea cows, which thrive on the plants, offer some hope of control.

Plants That Ran Wild

No less destructive—and difficult to deal with—than an animal invasion may be the unchecked growth of a plant. The prickly-pear cactus was brought to Australia to serve as range fence and emergency stock feed; before it was brought under control by means of an insect parasite it had taken over more than 60 million acres. In California, klamath, or goatweed, the European St. John's-wort, accidentally brought to the New World in the late 19th Century, by 1940 had invaded over a quarter-million acres of valuable pasture before it, too, was checked by insect parasites. No such insects have yet been found to control the water hyacinths that clog navigable channels in Louisiana, the Congo and elsewhere. A showy plant with orchidlike blooms, this hyacinth was brought from Venezuela for the New Orleans Cotton Exposition in 1884. Charmed by its beauty, visitors obtained clippings to set out in their ponds and streams. The tough and fast-growing plants soon spread to the rivers and canals, covering them from bank to bank and sometimes bringing traffic to a standstill.

IN LOUISIANA, dredges barely keep pace with rampant hyacinth growth. Since each plant may produce 1,000 offspring every 50 days, cutting or uprooting has only temporary effects.

4

Rhythms, Cycles and Clocks

"Thou canst not stir a flower without troubling of a star," stated the mystical poet Francis Thompson. He exaggerated the links in the fabric of life, but his was none the less a true insight into the fact that there do exist ecological relationships between living things here on earth and the movements of the heavenly bodies. Not only are earthly organisms affected by light and warmth from the distant moon and sun, but also many animals have been shown to possess mechanisms which accurately measure the sun's position and react to the rhythm of the tides, the phases of the moon and the motion of our planet. Even man is not so independent of the revolving cycles that operate upon all plants and animals as he would like to believe. Most of the plants he cultivates and the animals he domesticates show marked cycles of reproduction and feeding due to the varying amounts of daylight and darkness or to the passage of the seasons caused by planetary motion.

In a few environments—the darkness of caves, the soil, the depths of the sea —communities of life are largely sheltered from the cycles caused by the heavenly bodies. But elsewhere, they must contend with these rhythmic oscillations. Twice each day, at dusk and at dawn, there is a shift in the activity of the populations that inhabit a community, amounting to almost a complete turnover of the species. This is known as the diurnal cycle and it results from the spin of the earth on its axis, resulting in various degrees of light and darkness in each 24-hour period. The green plants carry on photosynthesis only during the daylight hours; the majority of fungi, which do not possess chlorophyll, grow as well in darkness as in light. Some kinds of animals are stimulated to activity by light; other kinds retreat from it. The difference between diurnal and nocturnal animals is a complex one—the end result of evolutionary adaptations, the physiology of the particular animals, their behavior. Mammals, for example, are generally more active at night, although there are notable exceptions that include mankind. Man's vision, like that of his closest relatives among the primates, is definitely adapted to daylight conditions; he also possesses color vision which requires more light than is usually available at night. Other kinds of animals are influenced in other ways by their evolutionary development or their bodily workings, with the result that they are committed to night, day, or the in-between world of dusk or dawn.

Thus most communities contain two sets of species, the diurnal and the nocturnal, which largely replace each other. At dusk, the daytime animals— most of the birds, insects and a majority of the lizards—settle down for the night and from there on a whole new world populates the darkness. Other kinds of birds appear, such as the owls, goatsuckers and oil birds, and most of the mammals become active. Primitive insects like the cockroaches and termites are nocturnal, but the more modern species—bees, wasps and butterflies—have become associated with modern flowering plants and hence are active during daylight hours when most flowers are open. The nocturnal moths are closely related to butterflies, but they are an exception: they feed upon the nectar of those flowers, usually white or pale yellow in color, that open at night. Some animals, such as the squirrels, demonstrate parallel adjustments to day and night between closely related species. Flying squirrels belong to the nocturnal community and they have colorless eye lenses; the diurnal gray and red squirrels, which may inhabit the same woods, have yellowish lenses. In both groups of squirrels, their differing times of activity are associated with this difference in the light-filtering ability of their eyes: they have adapted to the light intensities that exist during those hours of the daily cycle when they are active.

DAILY rhythms are clearly seen in the sea and large lakes. The myriads of small animals known as the zooplankton rise and fall in a rhythmic movement in the sea, coming to the surface at night and sinking during the day. As they rise they bring with them their pursuers, the larger animals, and the even larger ones which feed upon these. The steady rise and fall of the tiny plankton animals is thought to be influenced by many things—light, temperature, hunger, salinity of the water, gravity—but light seems to be a primary factor, since it may serve to alter the response of the animals to gravity. When light intensity is high, the animals are thought to be responsive to gravity and to sink; with increasing depth, the light grows fainter until finally the animal reaches a depth where the light stimulus no longer influences it, and it halts. As the intensity of the light wanes in the late afternoon, the response to gravity is reversed and the entire zooplankton population swims upward once more to feed at or near the surface upon the plant plankton, which have been producing energy during the daylight hours.

Another explanation for the vertical movement is that the plankton animals are attracted to particular bands of light intensity, rising or falling at different times of the day to avoid light of too great or too little intensity. One wonders what survival benefits they gain from all the energy expended in rising and falling. The animals certainly do not escape predators, for the predators too can move up and down. Possibly the answer lies in the advantages of movement between two different environments—the surface layer, which has strong currents, and the depths several hundred feet down, which do not. These drifting animals, with their weak powers of movement, thus can change from environment to environment merely by rising or sinking.

THE same general pattern occurs in large lakes, and careful study of the vertical movements of plankton animals in Lake Lucerne, in Switzerland, has shown the extent and speed of their vertical movements. There are differences between species and even between young and adults of the same species. The result is that the entire mass of minute animals does not attempt to crowd the topmost surface at the same hours of the night, nor does it disappear completely into the depths during the day. Instead, the differing responses to the different light intensities result in a vertical spreading out of the entire plankton community, and this stratification at varying depths leaves room for all.

Although many forms of life display fairly definite tendencies toward daytime or nighttime activity, many animals can alter their pattern in response to changing needs. A number of birds, such as warblers and some waterfowl, are distinctly diurnal in activity—but they migrate at night. The box turtle is active during the day, but female box turtles lay their eggs at night. Some members of a community, such as snails and slugs, may alter their behavior in response to wetness or dryness, although generally they find the moist conditions that are most favorable for them during the evening hours. Theodore Roosevelt pointed out that in regions where game is hunted persistently, the hunted animals tend to become nocturnal, whereas the same species is diurnal in areas where man has not made deep inroads. The North American mountain lion, the African lion and the Indian tiger have been observed to shift their prowling hours toward the night wherever they come into contact with their formidable enemy, diurnal man.

The round of the seasons, caused by the yearly circling of the earth around the sun, is an annual occurrence that never ceases to mystify and delight the beholder. Between the sleep of winter and the surge of spring, for example, it seems that all life is renewing itself as the snows melt and the sun rises daily higher in the sky. Buds burst and leaves unfurl, newborn animals crawl from their dens, the air fills with humming insects and returning birds. This seasonal cycle is most readily apparent in the woodlands of the Temperate Zone, but it exists everywhere and different kinds of communities react differently to the physical influences of the season.

Man often attributes the phenomena of the seasons—the migration and reproduction of birds, the turning of the leaves, the coming into bloom of wildflowers—solely to temperature, whereas the vital factor in many cases is actually the varying lengths of light and darkness in a day at different times of the year. Throughout the year, there is a difference in the proportion of daylight during each 24-hour period: there are maximum hours of daylight at the summer solstice in June and a minimum at the winter solstice in December. The varying amounts of light and darkness act as triggers upon the physiology

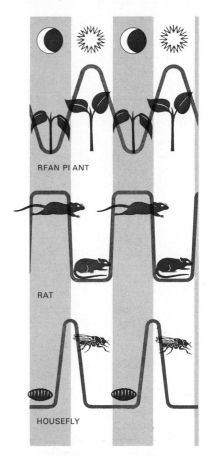

BEAN PLANT

RAT

HOUSEFLY

THREE BIOLOGICAL CLOCKS

The regularity with which biological clocks govern many of the activities of plants and animals is a constant and fascinating source of laboratory study. As seen in the graph above, for example, bean leaves turn limp at night, erect during the day. The graph of a rat's activity falls into a pit-shaped lull during daytime, leaps to a plateau at night. The great majority of houseflies emerge from their pupal cases in the morning. So strong are these behavioral adaptations that they persist even out of the normal environment, when conditions of light, temperature and moisture are controlled.

of numerous kinds of animals and plants, signaling them to many activities. A long-time mystery has been how the pupa of a silkworm moth, enclosed inside a thick cocoon, is informed that it is spring and time to awaken. The explanation is that some light does penetrate the dense cocoon and reaches the brain of the sleeping pupa through a transparent zone in its head. A sort of computer inside the pupa's brain "counts" the hours of darkness and daylight in each 24-hour day; as the length of the days increases in the spring, growth forces are set into motion that arouse the pupa from its winter sleep and transform it into an adult moth. While there are only eight hours of light in a day, as happens during the winter, the insect remains dormant, but with increasing hours of continuous daylight, 26 nerve cells in the brain secrete a hormone that awakens the insect to the outside world.

The seasonal changes in the coats of some mammals have also been found to depend upon the varying degrees of light and darkness and to be largely independent of temperature. By artificially shortening the hours of light in each 24-hour day, as happens naturally each autumn, scientists were able to change the color of the coats of two kinds of North American weasels from the brown of summer to the whitish coat of winter. When the duration of light was again artificially lengthened, the animals returned to their summer colors. It has even been possible to prevent altogether the appearance of the brown summer coat of the snowshoe hare by exposing the animal year round to an artificial winter light of nine hours a day—even when the temperature remained at a summery 70°F.

THE circle of the seasons actually consists of many circles of activity on the part of the members of the community. One of the most comprehensive analyses of seasonal events within a community, made several decades ago in Wisconsin, revealed at least 328 events—the blooming of forest, grassland and marsh plants, emergence from hibernation of local mammals, migration of birds and similar occurrences—affecting the community. Moreover, a study of the same community a dozen years later revealed that many of these seasonal events recurred rhythmically from year to year, although they might be early or late by a few days, as certain species assumed more important roles or as unusual weather retarded or advanced the parades of activity. Actually, although the seasons appear to proceed with great regularity, one June is rarely exactly like the following one, and that one most probably will be different from the June a year hence. Some years in June, certain insect members of the community are more or less abundant than in previous years; the wild-flower displays may be more startling or disappointing in their color and abundance. The seasonal cycle so well known in the temperate woodlands has its counterpart in the polar regions and in lakes, where there is a seasonal turning over of the water itself as the upper layer of water warms or cools. Certain parts of the tropics, instead of having hot and cold seasons, are characterized by the alternation of dry, or "winter," and rainy, or "summer" seasons. The wave of life in the tropics crests during the rainy season and reaches its trough during the dry, although the change is not so startling as in the so-called Temperate Zone with its more drastic seasonal changes.

Many people do not realize that there are also seasons in the oceans of the temperate latitudes, dependent upon solar radiation, water temperature and the cycles of various nutrients. When one looks at the sea, one hardly suspects the teeming numbers of small plant producers that drift on the surface; yet a

SEASONS' CHANGES IN SEA PASTURES

In their watery world, the diatoms are as much affected by changing seasons as are plants on land. Sunlight, minerals and temperature act strongly to influence them.

WINTER

In winter, essential minerals accumulate on the sea bottom—decaying organisms which died when lack of sunlight inhibited photosynthesis. Later, storms stir vertical currents, which carry them to the surface, to be absorbed by diatoms.

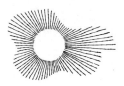

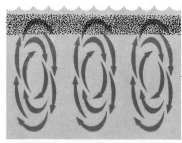

SPRING

Spring days mean longer hours of the sunlight needed for photosynthesis. With an abundant supply of dissolved nitrates and phosphates already in the upper layers of the oceans, the diatoms now have ideal conditions for maximum growth.

cubic foot of ocean water may hold 12.5 million chlorophyll-bearing plant cells. The microscopic diatoms are the most important photosynthetic producers of the community of the open sea, the pastures in which the sea animals graze. In winter, the surface waters are cold and poorly illuminated; diatom growth is inhibited. As the surface warms in spring with the northward travel of the sun, there is a sudden blooming of the diatoms, which make use of the abundant nutrients, particularly nitrates and phosphates, that were unused and accumulated during the winter. During this favorable time of the year, each little diatom can divide in half within the space of a day, and the two cells thus formed give rise to four the next day and to eight the following. By the end of a week a single diatom can produce 126 offspring. In the Gulf of Maine, for example, the number of diatoms may multiply 1,000 times between winter and spring, and in some especially favorable locations they may increase 60,000-fold.

THE diatom bloom also brings about a burst in the reproduction of the animal life of the plankton—the swarms of young barnacles, the larval stages of starfish, mollusks, worms and crustaceans, the copepods of the open sea and even young fish. They all partake of the rich pasturage floating in the sea and of the small creatures that feed directly upon the diatoms. Shortly thereafter the diatoms decline once again, not only because they have been devoured, but also because they largely have used up the store of nitrates and phosphates in the water. Then, in autumn, there is another period of diatom bloom, although not so great as in the spring, because temperatures are falling and there is a reduced light intensity. The reason for the autumn bloom is that the deep stirring of the water by autumn gales brings to the surface the nitrates and phosphates that have accumulated at the bottom from the decay of plants and animals during the summer.

SUMMER

By summer, the springtime burst of diatoms has used up the supply of nutrients. The colder, heavier, richer bottom waters cannot cross the temperature barrier to the surface; without replenishment, the upper layers of the sea are barren.

Most people conventionally think in terms of the four seasons, but ecologists studying communities in the temperate region of the globe usually refer to six distinct seasons, each with its own community compositions: winter, early spring, late spring, early summer, late summer and autumn. Thus bird communities in temperate zones do not closely parallel man's division of the year into four seasons: there are varying compositions of permanent residents, winter visitors and summer residents, with populations swelled in spring and autumn by transients on migration. In the Arctic, there are only two real seasons: a nine-month winter and then the three summer months of continuous daylight, during which the surface of the soil thaws and life seems to appear with a sudden rush. As one proceeds southward from the poles, seasonal differences become less and less due to temperature and more and more to wetness and dryness. In the Temperate Zone deserts, summer is the season in which life retreats, while it abounds in early spring and late summer. It is not only the feeding activity that is cyclic in the Temperate Zone, but also reproduction. Because the familiar domestic animals—the horses, sheep and cattle of the temperate grasslands—and the birds of the woodlands have their young in the spring and rear them during the most favorable seasons of plant growth, man tends to assume that all animals breed in the spring. But this is far from true: in the tropical rain forests, where the difference between seasons is not so pronounced, breeding occurs at various times of the year, depending upon the habits of the particular animals, and some kinds of animals breed around the seasonal calendar. Man is by origin a tropical animal, and like his primate

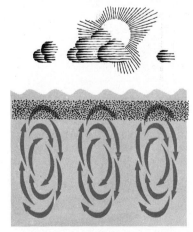

AUTUMN

Autumn's falling temperatures and rising gales once more rouse the ocean depths, destroy the temperature barrier and permit mixing of mineral nutrients. Since days are still long, there is a fresh burst of diatoms, though less than in spring.

relatives in the tropics, he has retained his nonseasonal mating habits no matter where he dwells on the globe.

In addition to the revolving earth and the distant sun, there is another planetary body which has great influence on living things—the moon. There has been no dearth of folklore about the influence of the moon on the growing of crops and upon human behavior, and indeed some of it may be grounded in fact. Humans and coyotes apparently do reach emotional heights under a full moon, and the 28-day menstrual cycle in the human female may be an evolutionary survival from mammalian ancestors that had rhythmic periods of heat in phase with the moon. The cycle of the intensity of moonlight during the month has been shown to affect the reproduction of some animals. The giant forest rat of Malaysia has a bimonthly cycle of a great number of pregnancies that appears to be in phase with the full moon; the onset of the period of bright moonlight near the time of full moon possibly stimulates these nocturnal animals to conception.

The primary influence of the moon, however, is the gravitational force it exerts with the sun on the seas of the world. The revolving moon results not only in the twice-daily tidal rhythms, but also in extremely high tides every 14 days, when the sun and moon are aligned with the earth and pulling together upon the waters. The major effect of the tidal rhythms is found among organisms that inhabit the shallow waters near shore; in fact, rhythms in this environment are more related to the tides than to the daily cycles of sunlight and temperature caused by the spinning and tilting earth.

THE most spectacular tidal rhythms are to be found among the segmented worms, which are related to the familiar earthworms and leeches. A clamworm, for example, which inhabits the Atlantic coast of North America, spawns twice each month during the summer—at the full moon and again at the half-moon. The large palolo worms of the South Pacific, which inhabit holes among the coral reefs, also swarm and breed at definite phases of the moon and tide, which of course vary in different places. At the third quarter of the moon in October and November, the palolo becomes mature; eggs and sperm are concentrated in the hind ends of their bodies. At the appointed time, this hind end separates from the parent and swims to the surface, there to mate. So precise is the timing of some of these segmented worms that one kind almost always swarms around Bermuda exactly three days after the full moon and a precise 54 minutes after sunset. Even if stormy weather delays the swarming a few days, it does not affect the time of day.

Rhythms such as these appear even among higher animals, such as the fishes. Records of the herring fisheries off the east coast of England show maximum catches at the periods of the full moon in October and November. A well-known example of rhythmic behavior is that of the grunion of the Southern California coast, which times its spawning precisely to the highest tides. Another kind of link between the moon and the living inhabitants of the shore is seen in a tiny flatworm that inhabits sandy beaches in Brittany and the Channel coast. This worm has formed a partnership with a green alga. The algae inhabit the surface cells of the worm and are responsible for the worm's rich green color; during most of its life the food supply of the worm is derived solely from the sugar energy produced by its partner through photosynthesis, and the alga, in turn, receives wastes from the worm.

The algal partner is also paid by being given mobility, since to carry on

THE MOON AND THE PALOLO

In the peculiar reproductive process of some worms—such as the Pacific palolo (above), which lives in coral reefs—the timing is controlled by the moon. The sex organs of the mature adults always ripen once a year at about the same time on the same day when the moon is in its last quarter. Then the organs split off with the worm's posterior section (unshaded), which swims to the surface. There the eggs and sperm are shed into the water and fertilization occurs. This section of the worm then dies; the head and upper half of its body (shaded), however, remain in the coral holes and develop new reproductive organs for the next year.

photosynthesis, it must be brought to the sunlight. Thus, as soon as the tide ebbs each day, these worms emerge by the millions, forming large bright green splashes on the wet yellow sand left by the retreating tides. During the several hours while the tide is out, the worms lie moist and glistening in the sun; the little plants in the worms' tissues produce the sugars and starches necessary for their mutual existence. As the tide rolls up the beach once again, the green patches seem miraculously to disappear as the worms retreat into the sands. The entire life of the worm is a succession of vertical movements—upward on the ebb tide, downward on the flow.

The remarkable thing about this unusual partnership is not so much that both producer and consumer in a food chain are intimately united, but rather the enduring nature of the worm's vertical movements. When these worms are captured and kept in an aquarium, where no tidal rhythms can possibly exist, the worms nevertheless continue to rise each day out of the sand and into the light, later sinking into the darkness. This worm is too low in the evolutionary ladder to possess a brain capable of much memory, yet far removed from its native surf it still continues faithfully to live out the rhythm of the distant sea.

In recent years, other organisms have been found that respond to rhythms apparently connected to the sun, moon or tides—rhythms which persist even when the organisms are isolated from the very causes of these rhythms. The governing of vital activities—feeding or reproduction—for a wide assortment of animals has been shown to be regulated by what have been called "biological clocks," although no one is certain where they exist in the animal or how they work. A number of kinds of animals—species of birds, turtles, shrimps, bees and others—navigate by taking fixes on the celestial bodies. To navigate in this way, the animals would seem to require not only a good memory for the position of certain stars or the sun's course, but also a reliable timepiece that tells them how much the earth has revolved while the sun and stars seem to be moving across the sky. Organisms possessing such built-in biological clocks have the advantage of being able to "anticipate" the rhythms and thus alter their way of living before the actual changes take place. A bee, for example, uses its internal clock to arrive exactly on time for the opening of a flower it visited the day before; and the very flower it visits also uses some sort of internal timing mechanism that tells it the time of day to open its blossoms. Indeed, the workings of an internal clock can be observed in many humans who set their alarm for the same hour each day; after several days they get in the habit of awakening *before* the alarm goes off.

ONE of the most startling cases of an internal clock that is able to continue ticking independent of the environment is that of the fiddler crab, a common species on many beaches, named for the oversized pincer with which the male seems to make fiddling motions. The fiddler crab reveals a striking cycle of color changes—dark during the day, pale in early evening, darkening again toward daybreak. There may be survival benefit for the crab in this color change, with the darker daytime color helping to conceal it in the shadows from predators and perhaps also protecting it against the effects of strong sunlight; the point here is that when the degree of darkening was measured and plotted on a graph for 16 days, it was noticed that the degree of greatest darkening took place about 50 minutes later each day. It was next seen that the maximum darkening of the crabs kept captive in the laboratory came at about the same time of day when the tide was low in the place where they had been collected, and the maximum lightness at the time of high tides. Further experiments revealed that at the very same time that the crabs in their natural environment on the beach were taking on their darkest color, their relatives in the laboratory—which had been kept in a dark room for as long as a month—also reached their darkest color, persisting in their natural rhythm even though they saw no sun. More remarkable still was the difference in behavior of fiddler crabs captured at Cape Cod and at Martha's Vineyard. This island is only some five miles away from Cape Cod, but the tides occur there about four hours later each day—and the island's crabs in the laboratory in fact turned their darkest color exactly four hours later than the crabs captured at Cape Cod.

The ability of shore animals to maintain their tidal rhythms in the absence of the tides themselves has been confirmed elsewhere. A large variety of sea animals, including fishes, was studied in the coastal waters of Brittany, France, where the tidal range is considerable. In their natural environment, it was found that these organisms showed a rhythmical increase and decrease in oxygen consumption not correlated with the hours of the day, but rather with the rhythms of the tidal cycle. Taken to the laboratory for study, these animals continued the rhythm in the tideless aquarium, sticking with great tenacity to the natural sequence of the tides along their native shores for weeks afterward, just as if they were free.

A T present, the whole question of internal clocks is still a mystifying one and a bone of contention among various scientists. There is no shortage of theories. One group of scientists believes that the biological clocks are regulated by forces outside of the animal, just as the man-made clock does not work unless it is plugged into an electrical circuit or hand-wound. This view has been supported by experimental proof that these biological clocks can be reset, for example, by juggling the hours of light and darkness and thus creating "days" of less than 24 hours. Suggestions for possible external sources that operate the clocks have been the earth's magnetic field, changes in barometric pressure or even in cosmic radiation. Another belief holds that the protoplasm of life itself possesses these internal, self-contained timepieces, which evolved as an advantage for organisms possessing them in adjusting their feeding or reproduction precisely to natural rhythms in the environment. This view also has been sustained. Experiments have proven that these behavioral rhythms often persist long after the organisms have been removed from every one of the environmental factors that ecologists consider might be of importance. Whichever of these explanations—or even other possibilities—is correct, there is no doubt that the timepieces do exist and that they are widespread throughout the living world.

Man, as an animal, also apparently possesses a number of built-in rhythms, and his body chemistry has been shown to operate in a rhythmic pattern. Even during the sleep of a human, there is an inexplicable 90-minute cycle of electrical activity in the brain. The recent discoveries about biological clocks add still another apparently invisible restraint upon the actions of living things. Not only are animals and plants fenced in by ecological barriers, their habitats delineated by competition and partnerships, their niches determined by adaptations—but also even their behavior patterns within this labyrinth of interactions are governed by subtle internal responses to the distant, revolving heavenly bodies.

BY MARKING ZEBRAS AND THEN TRACKING THEM BY PLANE, SCIENTISTS GAIN INSIGHT INTO THE ROUTES AND TIMING OF THEIR MIGRATIONS

The Puzzling Timers

The more scientists investigate the internal clocks of many plants and animals, the more complex and fascinating their research becomes. What is the mechanism that makes these clocks run? Can it be localized, or does it pervade the entire organism? Is it autonomous—or influenced by outside forces? The answers still lie hidden in the behavior of animals like those shown on the following pages.

INITIAL CONTACT is made as two hermaphroditic land snails brush mouths and feelers together preparatory to mating.

A NUPTIAL DANCE, elaborately conducted in slow motion, may preoccupy the paired snails for as long as two hours.

AFTER CROSS-FERTILIZING EACH OTHER, THE LAND SNAILS WILL LAY THEIR EGGS IN THE GROUND. DESPITE ELABORATE BUILT-IN PRECAUTIONS,

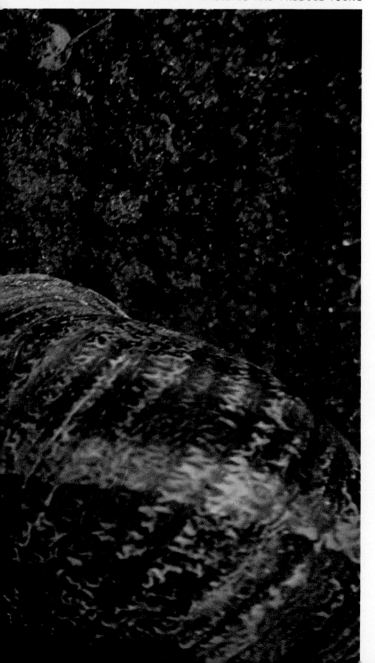

AS THE DANCE PROGRESSES, the snails shoot sharp darts of calcite at each other, which seems to increase stimulation.

SNAILS MAY SOMETIMES FERTILIZE THEMSELVES AND PRODUCE YOUNG

Slugs, Snails and the Seasons

The fact that certain primitive creatures—for instance, slugs, common night-foraging inhabitants of gardens—lay their eggs on schedule, year after year, may not at first seem surprising, until one considers that this might involve an internal clock able to keep time for a whole year. And indeed, some slugs, when kept in the laboratory without discernible cues from nature under controlled conditions of light, temperature and humidity, go right on doing what they have been doing regularly in the wild: spinning out, with the onset of August, strings of clear, gemlike eggs.

The land snail, a relative of the shell-less slug, may also possess such a clock to help it carry out a complex reproductive process. Equipped like the slug with both male and female organs, the snail produces sperm throughout the warmest part of the year, but carries eggs for only a limited period. This may serve to protect the land snails, whose mating behavior and reciprocal fertilization are shown on these pages, from fertilizing themselves during the months of their greatest activity. Although mating takes place in May or June, these snails do not lay eggs until July or August. It is believed that for at least part of this time the foreign sperm remains stored in a pouch while the snail's own sperm degenerates, thus assuring that when the mature eggs pass down a common duct into the pouch, they will not be accidentally self-fertilized on the way.

NEWLY HATCHED SNAILS feed on lettuce. Before winter, they will bury themselves, seal their shells and wait for spring.

85

INCUBATING GRUNION EGGS AWAIT THE TIDE

Time, Tide and the Grunion

To that well-known little fish of California's coastal waters, the grunion, the rhythm of the tides means survival as a species. In the dramatic manner in which they accomplish their spawning, the highest night tides, from March to August, play a vital role. As the tide begins to ebb, the grunions splash onto the beaches, the female wriggling tailfirst into the sand to deposit her eggs safely below the surface. After the male has fertilized them, both are washed out to sea again.

By spawning when the tide is running out, rather than coming in, the grunions assure that their eggs will lie undisturbed in the sand until the water again rises to the highest tide level two weeks later. During this period, the eggs go through the developmental stages shown below. When waves at last churn them from the sand, their membranes rupture and the fully formed fish are released to the sea.

THRUST ONTO A BEACH BY A WAVE, SHIMMERING GRUNIONS RUSH TO MATE

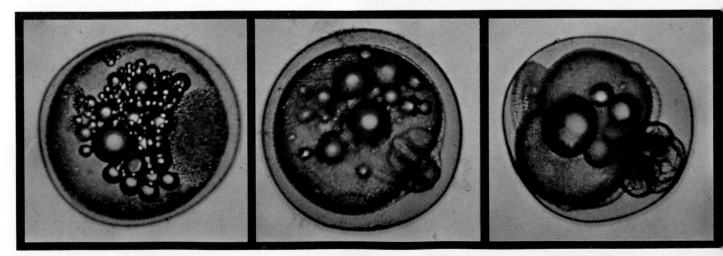

15 HOURS   56 HOURS   89 HOURS

BEFORE ANOTHER WAVE WASHES THEM BACK INTO THE PACIFIC. THE FEMALES PROTRUDE HEADFIRST FROM THE SAND AS THEY LAY THEIR EGGS

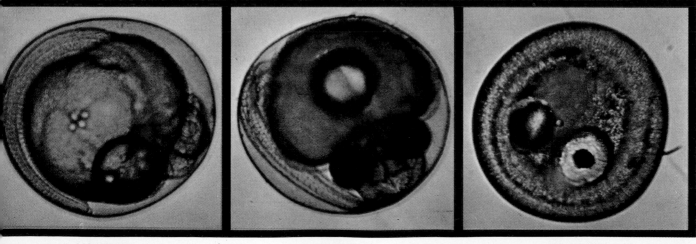

112 HOURS   160 HOURS   NINE DAYS

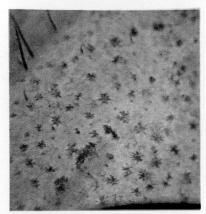

NIGHTTIME COLORING of the fiddler crab is several shades lighter than the daytime coloring (*below*). The change takes place when spots of dark pigment in the shell concentrate, forming the star shapes in the close-up above.

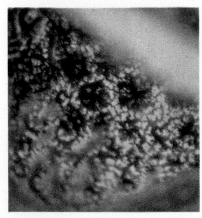

BY DAY, the fiddler crab has a dark shell, spotted all over with dispersed pigments, as in the enlargement of its shell above. A hormone manufactured in the crab's eyestalks is instrumental in affecting the daily color changes.

The Mysterious Fiddler Crab

A mystery of the marshlands and sandy flats of the intertidal zone is the color change of the fiddler crab. Whether the change serves to camouflage this jaunty little creature, or protect it from the sun's ultraviolet rays, or perhaps regulate its temperature, no one has yet been able to discover. There is no doubt, however, that the change in coloration, from pale at night to dark by day, is closely related not only to the daily cycle of the sun but to the tides as well.

Yellowish-white throughout the night, the crab begins to darken around sunrise in keeping with the 24-hour rhythm of its color change. It does not become maximally dark, however, until low tide— the period in the day when it is most active. Then it tunnels to the surface and saunters forth into air and sun in a dark coat produced by a dispersal of the pigments in its shell. Thus colored, it forages on algae and other microorganisms laid down on the mud by the retreat of the tide. The peak of its color will come exactly 50 minutes later each day, reflecting the 24-hour, 50-minute tidal rhythm.

LIKE A MARAUDING ARMY, fiddler crabs scuttle across a Cape Cod marsh in search of food. Often marshes are colonized by two species of fiddler crabs, but rarely do they invade each other's territory, even when one territory is uninhabited. This is because each species shows an inherited preference for sand or mud, as the material in which to make its burrows.

UNDER UMBRELLAS shielding them from direct light, snails are observed in an experiment on magnetism. The snails, it was found, do respond to magnetism—and may use the magnetic field of the earth for orientation.

What Is the Driving Force?

How to settle the controversy over whether the clock that tells grunions when to spawn and fiddler crabs when to change color is autonomous or regulated externally? Experiments with plants and animals, in which light, pressure and temperature are rigidly controlled, seem the best way; yet evidence still suggests that they receive information from the outside, anticipating, for instance, drops in barometric pressure up to two days in advance. Other experiments, like those shown here, explore geophysical forces as a possibly decisive factor.

SNAILS WITH STRINGS attached to them twitch levers of a recording device as they crawl around in laboratory dishes. They are being observed for clues as to how they time their activity to correspond with high tide.

CHIEF INVESTIGATOR of the influence of geophysical forces on internal clocks, Dr. Frank Brown of Northwestern University checks a device used to record the breathing of crabs kept in hermetically sealed tanks in a dark room. Even under such controlled conditions, their breathing continues to follow tidal rhythms—coming to a maximum an hour before low tide.

A SONIC TAG is clipped onto the back of a salmon to transmit data to a receiving set *(below)*. Thus scientists can track the fish on part of its spawning trip, from ocean to home stream.

Tracking Down the Answers

The mysterious influences—autonomous or external—that help birds and fish to navigate may yet be uncovered by a new research tool. Scientists are now tracking salmon and homing pigeons with electronic devices—tiny sonic "tags" that radio their movements. Strapped to the back of a pigeon *(opposite)*, a minute but powerful transmitter weighing less than an ounce beams back to two stations sufficient directional data to enable investigators to plot the exact flight path of the bird. Improvements in the transmitter may soon allow them to monitor changes in the environment and the bird's reactions to them. Thus, by correlating the environmental data with the physiological data, they hope to unravel the secrets of the homing pigeon's navigation.

TUNING IN on the movements of electronically tagged salmon with a receiving set, scientists seek to follow and record the positions of the fish in the water. Such equipment may be used in lakes to track fish and yield information on their behavior with respect to ecological conditions. Other tracking devices include tags that pick up and relay metabolic changes.

RELEASING A HOMING PIGEON WEARING A TRANSMITTER, SCIENTISTS READY RECEIVER AND ANTENNA TO FOLLOW ITS FLIGHT

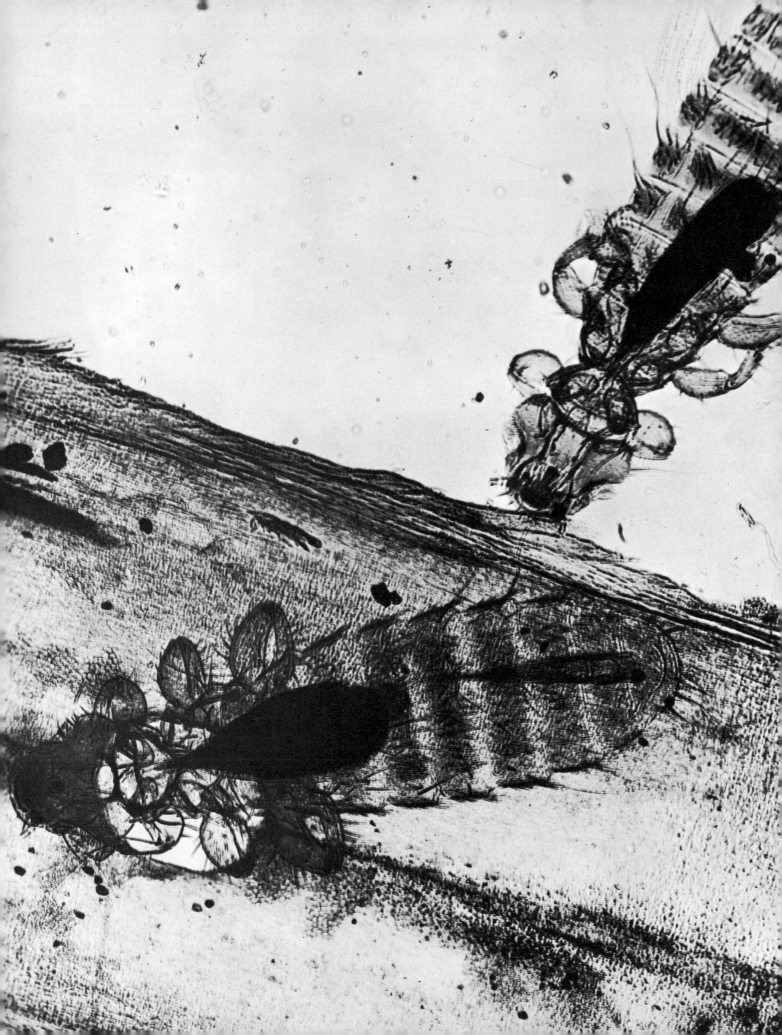

5

Mutual Aid—
or Tooth
and Claw?

BIRDS," wrote the British scientist A. E. Shipley, "are not only birds but
aviating zoological gardens." The range of tiny creatures that birds carry
aloft with them is truly impressive: their feathers are eaten by lice and mites,
their skin by certain flies; fleas, lice, mosquitoes, leeches, ticks and others suck
their blood from the outside while protozoa destroy their red blood corpuscles
from the inside; varieties of parasitic worms are located in practically every organ
of a bird's body. From the time that it is born in its snug nest, which is also a favorable habitat for intruders, the hatchling encounters the grim realities of parasitism. One study of the nests of 56 species of birds revealed the presence of no
less than 529 different kinds of arthropods—most of them mites and beetles.
Throughout its life, the bird is attacked by representatives of nearly every group
of parasitic animals, ranging from one-celled microorganisms up the evolutionary
ladder to birds themselves—such as the European cuckoo, American cowbird
and African honey guide—which induce other birds to feed and rear their
broods for them. Not only do a wide variety of parasites attack birds, but also the
numbers of any single parasitic species are often extremely high: more than
1,000 feather lice, for example, were taken from the plumage of a single curlew.

A PROBLEM OF HOUSING

🌸 fungus		〰 tapeworm	
amoeba		tongue worm	
flagellate		leech	
plasmodium		bug	
spirochete		flea	
trypanosome		feather louse	
encapsulated tongue worm		fly larva	
fluke		louse fly	
roundworm		mite	
spiny-headed worm		tick	

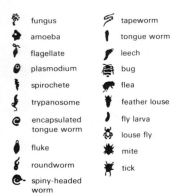

From the moment it hatches, a bird is subject to invasion by one or more of the 20 parasites shown here: external fleas, flies, ticks and mites, and internal worms and flukes as well as microscopic protozoa, fungi, bacteria and viruses, some of which are transmitted by the bites of mosquitoes and flies. By dust bathing and preening, the host holds down their numbers on the feathers and skin, and special blood cells and antibodies fight to prevent overcrowding in the lungs, liver, trachea and blood. If this balance is upset, the parasites take over, bringing disease and often death to the host.

One ordinarily thinks of death coming to an animal by the swift stroke of a predatory beak or claw—but actually the living world swarms with animals which, because of their small size, can live inside or on the surface of the host and eat it little by little. The very word "parasite" means "one who eats beside another." Although most laymen, and even some biologists, look upon parasites with repugnance, the importance of these forms of life cannot be avoided. To an ecologist studying a community, there is little difference in the flow of energy between a rabbit nibbling on a plant and a tick sucking the blood from that same rabbit—or even a microbial parasite feeding on that same tick. The extent of parasitism is truly remarkable, as was pointed out by Jonathan Swift:

> *So, naturalists observe, a flea*
> *Hath smaller fleas that on him prey;*
> *And these have smaller still to bite 'em;*
> *And so proceed ad infinitum.*

In fact, so widespread is parasitism that the only living things free from it at all are the few final parasites in these long chains. Man himself, like any animal, actually represents a habitat complete with numerous niches that are sometimes filled by parasites. Nerve and muscle tissue, the lungs, glands and digestive system are all habitats for at least one kind of parasite and usually many. So delicate are their adaptations that certain kinds of lice inhabit hair on the head, while completely different kinds inhabit hair on other parts of the body. Almost all groups of plants and animals have their wayward species that have taken the road to parasitism, but it becomes increasingly common the lower one goes in the evolutionary ladder. Several groups of lower animals, particularly among the flatworms, nematodes and arthropods, are wholly parasitic. Among vertebrates, however, parasitism as a way of life is extremely rare. Among plants it is common in the fungi, but there are a few parasitic species even among the higher, flowering plants—notably the mistletoe and dodder.

ANYONE can identify a body louse as a parasite, but usually there are confusing borderline cases and subtle shadings in these relationships. Certain animals —such as the protozoa which cause bird malaria—must live as parasites throughout their entire lives and cannot exist apart from their hosts. But others, notably ticks and mosquitoes, are parasitic usually only at single stages in their lives and spend most of their time in the free state. Some parasites are fully capable of living their lives as free animals, but resort to parasitism if a host becomes available. The subject is still further complicated by the fact that many living things form associations that, far from being harmful, are actually beneficial for both partners, as in the case of the lichen formed by a partnership between a fungus and an alga. In other cases, partners live together largely oblivious of each other, although usually one of the partners manages to extract some benefit from the relationship. Some scientists believe that these mutually beneficial or neutral relationships began originally as parasitic ones but evolved into truces. Other scientists think that although mutual partnerships appear to be in balance now, they will eventually disintegrate and lead to the success of one partner over another, and that parasitism will result.

Ever present in any parasitic relationship is the fact that the parasite must make a compromise: it must restrict its activities so that it does not immediately endanger its host's life and thus deprive itself of a food supply as well as the opportunity for the reproduction of its own kind. The ideal way of life for a parasite, of course, is not to bring about permanent injury in its host; if the parasite allows the host to live out its life and to reproduce successfully, the host furnishes offspring for future generations of parasites. Some parasites that cause human diseases attract attention simply because they are the exceptions —they have not achieved this ideal balance. Despite the lengthy list of well-known human diseases caused by parasites, comparatively few of them remain severe for long periods of time in a single part of the globe—for if the human host dies too quickly, so does the parasite. In fact, as a parasite evolves, it usually becomes weaker rather than more virulent; at the same time the host becomes gradually immune or develops resistance in the form of antibodies that neutralize the invading organisms. Thus, both the parasite and the host achieve a way of living together that, although not harmonious by human standards, at least results in the survival of both.

ALL parasites face one difficult problem   they or their offspring must get from one host to another in order to ensure survival of their own species. They have solved this problem in numerous ingenious ways by the development of extraordinarily complex life histories. For example, a tapeworm that inhabits the intestines of a fox sheds its minute eggs into the intestinal tract of the host. These eggs fall to the ground in the fox's feces; the problem now is how they will get inside another fox. This is accomplished in stages that involve an intermediate host or hosts. A rabbit nibbles a plant on which the tapeworm eggs have fallen; the eggs hatch into larvae that bore their way into the rabbit's tissues, where they go into a resting stage, or cyst. If the rabbit is then eaten by a fox, the cysts eventually reach the fox's intestines and there develop into young tapeworms, which begins the cycle all over again.

A complex life history such as this, however, represents an evolutionary dead end for a parasite. The more fit the parasite becomes for life in the peculiar environment of its particular host, the more completely unfit it becomes for life in any other environment. It can continue to evolve further in only one direction—to a still more restricted parasitic niche. It is highly unlikely that any free-living organisms on the planet today evolved from ancestors that were parasites.

As a primitive creature, man once served as prey for other animals, but nowadays it is a rare event indeed when a human is killed by a lion, crocodile or shark. Humans today are among the very few species of animals relatively immune to predation. Man has been able to cope with his larger enemies, but the small ones have been another matter; the little parasites that feed on him have continued to flourish. When there is obvious harm, man acknowledges the presence of a parasite with the label "disease"; the parasite causing the disease is known as a "pathogen," derived from two Greek words that mean "bearer of suffering." Most of the intruders that inhabit the environment of the human body cause trouble, although there are exceptions—the bacteria in man's digestive system, for instance, seem to be helpful collaborators in synthesizing vitamins that he then absorbs. But most alien species absorb food and other materials needed by man's own body, and the very fact that they inhabit his tissue is likely to upset the operation of his nerves, muscles and other organs. More important, substances the parasites excrete in their own metabolism may act as poisons to man. Among the numerous diseases for which bacteria are responsible are scarlet fever, pneumonia, tuberculosis, diphtheria, bubonic plague, cholera, syphilis and whooping cough. Viruses are responsible for small-pox, polio, yellow fever and influenza; fungi cause ringworm, various lung diseases and even the common ailment known as "athlete's foot"; strange animal-like microbes cause malaria, sleeping sickness and dysentery; nematodes are responsible for various worm diseases like hookworm and trichinosis. Despite this impressive list of ailments, human beings have grown in numbers and have become resistant to most parasites—and they did so thousands of years before parasites were known or the science of medicine was even considered.

Primitive man viewed disease as a spreading into the air of unpleasant odors from wounds or as divine vengeance; the shaman, or witch doctor, sought to relieve the patient by sorcery. But modern man possesses a misunderstanding of the natural history of disease nearly as great as that of primitive man. The success of sulfa drugs in the 1930s and of penicillin during World War II in treating infection, and the subsequent flood of antibiotics have led man to believe that he has conquered disease by the sorcery of drugs. Indeed many of the diseases that have plagued mankind appear to have been brought under control in recent decades. Streptomycin dramatically reduced the cases of tuberculosis; malaria was banished, hopefully forever, from the continental United States in 1950; there are now vaccines that protect against polio, measles, smallpox, tetanus, cholera and numerous other dreaded diseases. However, these victories are largely illusions. They do not take into account the fact that the microbial organisms themselves are capable of extraordinarily rapid evolutionary changes, resulting in new strains resistant to man's most potent drugs. The specter of resistance to drugs by a number of microbes believed totally conquered only a few years ago is rising. The tubercle bacillus, for example, is making a strong fight for survival; there are many tuberculosis patients for whom the possibility of cure with drugs has apparently been exhausted. "The resistant organisms, furthermore," stated the New York City health commissioner in 1963, "can be transmitted from one person to another, spreading a new and worse strain of tuberculosis." The same story is apparently true of the comeback of syphilis as a major disease, and there is a threat of severe outbreaks of influenza, perhaps as serious as those of only a generation ago, in the years ahead.

ONLY recently has man come to understand the true cause of most diseases: a disturbance of the ecological environment. Speed of travel and penetration into remote areas by man have now converted most of the planet into a single environment, so far as disease organisms are concerned. Today the infectious diseases of Europe, North America, Australia and New Zealand are almost identical. Many of these diseases, however, are reaching—or have already reached—an approximate state of equilibrium with their human hosts in much the same way that, in other environments, other kinds of plants and animals achieve an eventual equilibrium. Thus, even before the advent of the wonder drugs, many of the common diseases of childhood, for example, had already begun to show steadily decreasing death rates. How, then, can one account for the catastrophic epidemics to which man is still falling prey?

When a host species is adjusted precisely to an undisturbed environment, its population tends to remain fairly constant and at a level lower than the potential "carrying capacity" for that environment. In such a situation a disease organism has difficulty in getting from host to host. However, if an environmental disturbance should cause a species to increase its numbers markedly, this would reduce one of the major problems of the parasite—the migration from host to host. When the population becomes dense, the pathogen can migrate easily and the result is an epidemic. The outbreak ends finally when the host population has been so decimated that once again it is scattered and the pathogen has difficulty in finding new hosts. Since man first climbed down from the trees, he had been disturbing his environment markedly: he has concentrated his populations in villages and eventually in metropolises, and thus few pathogens have been allowed to reach a state of equilibrium in all parts of the planet. Most of the diseases that plague mankind today are "civilized" diseases; it is difficult to visualize their having had much importance when the population of humans was low and scattered.

These "civilized" diseases have an ancient history in the congested Mediterranean world and in densely populated parts of Asia. Wherever civilized man has spread, he has taken them with him. Before the arrival of Europeans, many of the islands of the Pacific were densely populated, but the natives were unusually healthy, having had a long time in which to come to terms with the diseases found in their part of the world. However, they had no resistance to alien diseases. This, plus their concentrated populations, made them ripe for the epidemics touched off by the arrival of explorers, traders and missionaries. Epidemics of at least a dozen European diseases reduced the populations of some islands—as, for example, New Hebrides—to a tenth of their original number. The hardy Yahgan Indians of Tierra del Fuego numbered approximately 3,000 at the time Charles Darwin visited there on the H.M.S. *Beagle* in 1832; various introduced diseases have reduced their numbers to but half a dozen survivors at present. As recently as 1952, measles struck the Eskimos of the Canadian Arctic, attacking 99 per cent of the population. Even today, the natives of isolated Easter Island are subject to an annual influenza outbreak which occurs like clockwork for a month or two after the yearly visit of a Chilean warship to inspect the administration of the island.

· Television and movie epics to the contrary, it was not the pioneer who subdued the American Indian, but rather smallpox. European settlers in North America soon became aware that smallpox was one of their best weapons against the Indians and they even intentionally spread the disease by means of infected blankets. Long before this, smallpox also contributed to the defeat of Carthage by the Romans, and Napoleon's defeat in Russia was due as much to the losses his army suffered from typhus as to the hardships of winter. "Swords and lances, arrows, machine guns, and even high explosives have had far less power over the fates of nations than the typhus louse, the plague flea, and the yellow fever mosquito," wrote Dr. Hans Zinsser, who developed the vaccine against typhus, adding, with perhaps more enthusiasm than accuracy, "Soldiers have rarely won wars. They more often mop up after the barrage of epidemics."

Not only are the effects of disease dispersal visible in man himself; they also can be seen in his crops and domestic animals, and even in the natural world around him. The American chestnut tree was once among the largest and most numerous native hardwoods east of the Mississippi River; it was adapted to the varied demands of its community, and in many places it was the dominant tree in the forest. China has a chestnut tree also, and a fungus blight as well, but in the course of time the tree and the fungus have adjusted to each other and they both survive. However, at the beginning of this century the fungus blight became introduced accidentally into North America. The native chestnut possessed no immunity to the parasite, and the blight spread with explosive force. For all practical purposes, the chestnut no longer plays a major part in the forests it once dominated; today it appears doomed as a native North American

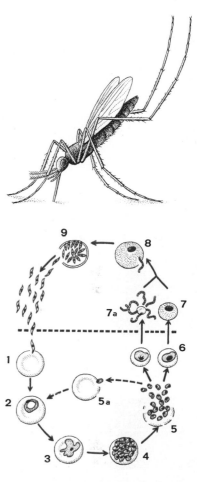

MALARIA AND THE MOSQUITO

The female Anopheles mosquito (at top) is the carrier of Plasmodium, a microscopic endoparasite which causes malaria in birds, man and other mammals. The malarial cycle (above) begins as the endoparasite invades a red blood cell (1). There it develops through "ring" and ameboid stages (2, 3), undergoes asexual division (4) and finally causes the cell to rupture (5). The released malarial spores either reinfect new blood cells (5a) or develop into sexual forms (6). The latter, sucked up by a mosquito, develop into sperm and egg cells (7a, 7), undergo fertilization (8) and change into a cyst (9). The cycle begins anew when the mosquito bites again.

species. There are, however, old stumps that continue to send up thin sprouts, and no one can be certain whether the final outcome will be complete extinction or the eventual evolution of a race of chestnut trees that are naturally resistant to the blight.

An example of a disease that *had* reached an equilibrium with its hosts in Australia, but suddenly gave rise to outbreaks in humans in North America and Europe about 1930, is psittacosis or "parrot fever." Thorough investigation of the outbreaks revealed that the pathogen, an animal-like microbe, is widespread as a mild disease among birds in the Australian wild. But it did not become a pressing human concern until parakeets and cockatoos were captured in their native haunts, kept in crowded aviaries and reared in quantity for sale as pets. This total disruption of the relationship between the birds and the microorganism tipped the equilibrium temporarily in favor of the microbe. Although the disease is still commonly known as parrot fever, it has since been learned that it mildly affects a variety of other birds besides members of the parrot family. In fact, psittacosis is undoubtedly a very ancient, almost universal infection of birds which long ago reached an equilibrium with its hosts—and flared up dangerously again only when man created an artificial environment for captive birds.

INFECTIOUS diseases—whether in man, other animals or plants—merely represent a widespread tendency of all living things to obtain what they need by preying upon the constructive labors of others. In fact, one might take the view that the whole living world consists of an endless chain of parasites and predators. This view was widely put forth in the Victorian era when Thomas Huxley summed up one current opinion about the discoveries of Charles Darwin and Alfred R. Wallace in regard to survival of the fittest. Wrote Huxley: "From the point of view of the moralist, the animal world is on about the same level as a gladiator's show. The strongest, the swiftest and the cunningest live to fight another day . . . no quarter is given." One of the leading poets of the age described a "Nature red in tooth and claw." On the other hand, many upheld the opposite extreme: an idealistic view of "mutual aid" between living partners became a cornerstone of anarchistic thought. Darwin himself leaned toward the view that parasitism might be replaced eventually by more equitable partnerships: "In numberless animal societies," he concluded, "the struggle between separate individuals for the means of existence disappears; struggle is replaced by cooperation."

The more one studies the varieties of parasitism and other relationships between animals and plants, the more one discovers that there are indeed strange bedfellows in the world of nature. The opposite extreme from parasitism is an ideal relationship between living things, known as mutualism, in which there is a partnership beneficial for both, although in practice one partner usually exercises a slightly greater degree of control. One obvious example of plant-animal mutualism is found in many flowering plants: they entice insects and other pollinators to visit them by offering nectar and pollen, thus ensuring themselves cross-fertilization. There is even a mutualistic relation of sorts between man and some of his food plants; corn is no longer found living in the wild state and probably could not survive without man's help. So intimate have many mutualistic partnerships become that the partners have developed various devices to make sure that the offspring of the partnership will carry on the same relationship. The female of a wood-boring beetle, for example, carries with her a fungus that grows in the cavity she inhabits and which softens the tough wood fibers; as her eggs are laid, she takes care to smear each one with fungus spores, thus ensuring that the partnership will endure in the next generation.

A classic example of varying degrees of partnership can be seen along many beaches. The little hermit crab, possessing a soft and vulnerable shell, protects itself by moving into an abandoned snail shell of the proper fit. The narrow end of the snail shell is often the abode of a small segmented worm that helps keep the inside of the shell clean and, in repayment, snatches fragments of food from the crab. The crab may also obtain a small sea anemone from a nearby rock and place it on the back of the shell; the stinging cells in the tentacles of the anemone are a deterrent to predators upon the crab and in return the anemone receives transportation to new feeding grounds as the crab moves about.

The concessions that must be made by both partners, and the occasional precariousness of their partnership, can be seen clearly in the relations between leguminous plants (such as beans and peas) and bacteria. These legumes possess on their rootlets numerous swellings, or nodules, inhabited by certain soil bacteria. The bacteria derive much of their nourishment from the plant, but in return they are able to take nitrogen from the air, synthesize it into compounds and make them available to the plant in whose roots they grow. This is clearly a beneficial partnership for both the plant and the nitrogen-fixing bacteria, but for it to come into effect, a number of adjustments must be made by both partners. For the bacteria to establish itself on the plant's root, the root must secrete a substance at a certain stage in its development. This done, it is then necessary for the bacteria to have an adequate shelter on the root, and this is provided in the form of a nodule which the root grows—presumably stimulated to do so by the bacteria. However, the bacteria must exercise some restraint; they must not continuously encourage the root to form nodules, for this would deprive the plant of a proper root system and thus kill both plant and bacteria.

This beneficial partnership, however, stands at the threshhold of parasitism and it can be upset readily when conditions become unfavorable for the plant or the bacteria. If the plant grows in a soil that is deficient in boron, for example, the bacteria cease to fix nitrogen; instead, they turn upon the plant itself and feed upon it, becoming true parasites.

THERE are many gradations between the opposite poles of a beneficial mutualism and a parasitism injurious to one of the partners. The word "symbiosis" (literally "living together") is generally used to describe this whole spectrum of relationships. At one end of the spectrum is one of the few flowering plants that has turned to the totally parasitic way of life. *Striga*, or witchweed—widespread in Africa, southern Asia and Australia, and an accidental invader of North America in 1956—is a root parasite of members of the grass family, particularly corn, but also sugar cane, sorghum, crabgrass and others. Deceptively beautiful with its bright green leaves and shiny scarlet or yellow blossom, it is one of the world's worst agricultural scourges. A single witchweed plant can produce up to half a million minute seeds barely visible to the naked eye and easily transportable by wind and rain. The seeds can lie viable in the soil for as long as 20 years, not germinating until a host appears.

The trigger for germination is a rare chemical substance which is given off by the roots of the grass plant as they spread out in the soil. If such a root should come within a tenth of an inch of a dormant witchweed seed, the chemical will not only stimulate the seed to start germinating, but also will provide a trail for

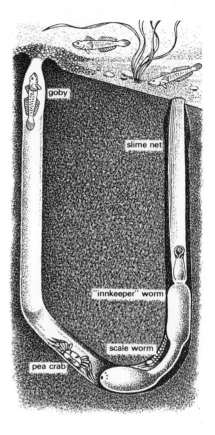

INNKEEPER'S GUESTS

The plump, foot-long "innkeeper" worm keeps house in the mud of shallow coastal waters for a motley collection of guests. The goby at the top is the least dependent on this commensal relationship. Though it is a regular lodger, it uses the burrow only for protection, foraging outside for its food. Further down in the tunnel a pea crab and a scale worm depend on their host for food and compete for the leftovers from the innkeeper's feasts. The innkeeper meanwhile feeds itself by spinning a transparent net of slime that fits over its head. Wavelike contractions of its body pump water bearing minute organisms through this net. Once full, both the net and its contents are gulped down whole—sometimes as often as every two minutes.

the witchweed's root to follow to the host's root. Once it reaches its destination, the witchweed attaches itself, then swells up and gives off an enzyme that softens the cell walls of the host root so that it can be penetrated. Fingerlike tentacles then emerge from the witchweed root, connect themselves to the internal plumbing system of the host and tap its water and nutrients. Witchweed lives underground as a complete parasite for three to eight weeks, sapping its host. It then appears above ground, quickly develops a green stem and leaves, and begins to manufacture its own food like any other respectable flowering plant. But it never completely abandons its connection to the host, depending upon it to furnish some minerals and water. A month later, witchweed flowers gracefully and produces seeds—which are tossed to the wind to sow the destruction of future crops.

A STEP above the true parasites are the partial parasites, such as mistletoe and dodder, which tap their host not only for a place in the sun but also for a water supply. Sometimes they absorb enough materials to cause a greatly reduced growth or even the death of the host, although they usually do little damage to a healthy plant. A further step away from true parasitism is found in the aerial plants, like some orchids of the tropical rain forests and Spanish "moss" (actually a member of the pineapple family), which gain benefits—chiefly a platform in the sun—from their hosts without harming them seriously or providing any benefits in return. Such a relationship, in which one partner benefits without serious harm to the other, is known as "commensalism" (literally "being at table together").

A good illustration of commensalism is provided by a kind of barnacle that attaches itself to the skin of a whale. The barnacle gets the benefit of a free ride and at worst affords only a slight hindrance to the whale by creating some drag on its movement through the water; in general, neither associate needs or seriously harms the other and each survives very well on its own. These ecological unions, though they may damage neither partner, usually benefit one of them by providing food, transportation, shelter or simply a foothold in a teeming environment. Some of these unions are most informal: a species of algae may grow as well on a turtle shell as on driftwood. Many kinds of bryozoa, or "moss animals," are found on the shells of mollusks and crustaceans; the association is usually a casual one, affording the guest only support. Some sedentary animals, however, derive great benefit from being attached to another animal rather than to an immobile rock: the host gives the guest the power of movement and also sets up currents of water that aid in feeding.

Commensalism is widespread at the seashore, and some of the most fascinating examples may be seen there, particularly in the case of animals that make burrows or tubes that also serve as homes for various guests that live by snatching surplus food from the host. There is a worm that lives in the mudflats on the California coast in a U-shaped burrow; the translation of its scientific name is "the fat innkeeper." And truly this worm has a strange assortment of tenants. The "innkeeper" feeds by trapping, in a bag of mucus, food particles that are washed into the burrow. Several small fishes live in the entrance of the tube in front of this feed bag, but they do not rob it; they use the burrow mainly for protection, emerging to feed. Living alongside the innkeeper may be found another kind of worm which does snatch some of the food from the bag. Behind the host usually lives a pair of tiny crabs, and in the wall of the burrow is sometimes embedded a small clam. These guests are not particular about the burrows they occupy; they may also be found in the burrows of two different kinds of shrimps.

Worms are not the only marine innkeepers. Several kinds of fishes live with impunity among the stinging tentacles of Portuguese men-of-war, anemones and medusas; some of them are known to achieve their immunity by nibbling on the tentacles, but in other cases the stinging animals may avoid using their tentacles when these particular fish species are present. The relationship of these small fishes to their hosts seems to have progressed from commensalism to mutualism: the fishes obtain protection and they pay for it by luring larger fishes within range of the tentacles.

The association between sharks and other fishes is well known. Pilot fish form small schools in front of sharks, picking up scraps of food dropped by their shark commensals. During the *Kon-Tiki* expedition across the Pacific, a school of pilot fish adopted the raft after their shark host was killed and they reacted to the raft as if it were a shark by swimming in front of it. The porous body of a sponge provides a home for a wide variety of sea creatures. One large specimen found growing off the Florida Keys served as a habitation of 13,500 other animals—some 12,000 of these were small shrimps, but the other 1,500 included 18 different species of worms, copepods and even a small fish.

Birds display almost every variation of symbiosis, from parasitism through the many gradations to mutualism. The cowbird with the bison of North America, the oxpecker with the antelope and rhinoceros of Africa—these are mutual associations in which the birds render considerable service to their hosts by ridding them of ticks and other external parasites and also serving as sentinels, at the same time receiving a constant food supply. These are true relationships and not accidental comings-together. An antelope, when visited by an oxpecker, will stand still, spread its legs and raise its tail—apparently to facilitate the work of these birds. A sleeping rhinoceros is easy to approach if no oxpecker is present, but a bird that is feeding on the animal will give an alarm. The osprey, a large fish-eating hawk, builds a permanent nest, usually on an old treetop, and year after year adds sticks atop it. A foot or two under the current year's section of the nest, the black-crowned night heron builds its own nest among the jumble of sticks and receives protection by living with the sharp-eyed hawk. Numerous other birds—grackles, wrens and sparrows—may also burrow into the sides of the nest under the watchful eye of the fish hawk, which does not interfere.

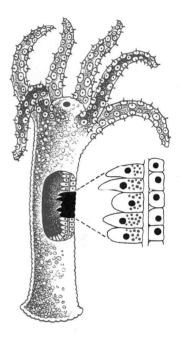

HELPFUL PARTNERS

A mutualistic partnership in the sea unites the green hydra, an animal, and a one-celled alga of the plant world. The alga, a zoochlorella, lives in cells lining the hydra's digestive cavity and supplies its host with food and oxygen. In turn, it receives protection and the substances it needs for photosynthesis.

THERE are also some relationships between birds and other animals which are seemingly inexplicable. The South American parakeet breeds only in the cartonlike nests of one species of termite on the branches of trees. While constructing its own hollow, the parakeet destroys approximately half of the termite nest. At first the termites attack the invader, but they soon accomodate themselves to the new situation—they do not molest the parent bird nor do they bite the vulnerable young. Rather, they extend their nest in a direction away from the damaged portion. Eventually, ants, the perennial enemies of the termites in the tropics, manage to enter through the damaged portion and finally expel the termites. What is so remarkable about this relationship is that the parakeet depends completely upon this single kind of termite, yet it inexplicably destroys half of the termite's nest and thus its own potential nesting site for the next breeding season. The termites are capable of preventing the successful breeding of this injurious parasite, yet they do not do so.

In other cases, birds have developed partnerships with insects for mutual benefit. One such arrangement concerns nest cleaning—and the silvery-cheeked hornbill of Africa harbors one of the most remarkable of insect cleaners in its nest. During the egg laying and brooding, the female hornbill is confined in a tree hollow by a wall of mud constructed by the male, leaving only a narrow slit. For 15 weeks the male feeds her and may bring her as many as 24,000 fruits to eat. Clearly, here is an opportunity for small animals to make a living and at the same time keep her nest clean. From the interior of a single nest 438 insects were obtained, belonging to eight species, two of them new to science. The interior of the nest was found to be clean and nearly odorless, certainly a tribute to the scavenging insects. That this was no mere accident, and that the hornbill's presence accounted for the presence of the insects, was proven the following year—a hornbill did not again occupy that hole, and the insect fauna was much scantier and composed of different species.

SOME birds are presumed to locate their nests in proximity to those of colonies of stinging social insects—such as wasps, ants and bees—for protection against humans and other predators. Others exploit bees in a different way, notably the sparrow-sized African honey guides, which have formed an alliance with the badgerlike ratel. Both the bird and the ratel seek the beehive—the ratel because of the honey and the larvae it contains, the bird because it is a wax eater. The honey guide, however, cannot attack and break open a hive, so it needs a partner like the ratel, which is nearly impervious to stings because of its tough, furry skin, which hangs loosely on its body. In return, the honey guide aids the ratel in locating the hives. When a honey guide finds a ratel in the forest, it attracts its attention by a loud chattering; the ratel follows it, issuing a series of grunts as if to reassure the bird that it is right behind it. Once the hive is located, the ratel tears it apart while the outraged bees furiously try to imbed their stingers; the bird waits on the sidelines and is content to eat the empty waxen combs after the ratel has finished with them.

So adaptable are these birds that they have learned to make use of baboons or even humans when no ratels can be found, attracting attention by chattering cries, fanning of their tails and display of their feathers. A honey guide may fly constantly around a human until he consents to follow it. Once he does, the bird makes a series of short fluttering flights, waits for the accomplice to catch up, then flies forward a little farther, all the time pouring forth an unbroken chatter. Dr. Herbert Friedmann of the Smithsonian Institution, an authority on the honey guides, has more than a score of times been waylaid by these birds and led to hives. These trips varied between 20 and 750 yards; the route taken was often a zigzag, and it is probable that the bird itself was not certain about the exact location of a hive when it started out. In some cases, honey guides have led accomplices to hives that had been abandoned by bees.

In the complex world of partners, accomplices and alliances, some of the larger birds of Africa, such as the marabou stork and long-crested hawk eagle, appear to team up occasionally with bees, building their nests right above the hives. The birds benefit from this—the bees protect their nests from nest parasites like the honey guides and from predators. What benefit the bees derive is not known. Much of this behavior is undoubtedly accidental, and the collaborations probably originated more by chance than by intelligence on the parts of the animals. "Although there is no evidence that any animal performs an action for the exclusive good of another," wrote Charles Darwin in *The Origin of Species*, "yet each tries to take advantage of the instincts of others."

SPARKLING TENTACLES TIPPED BY DROPS OF STICKY FLUID TRAP A LACEWING AS IT ALIGHTS ON THE FLOWER OF A CARNIVOROUS SUNDEW

Competition: Link to Life

All plants and animals are bound together by sharing the same earth, air and water. They are also linked by a competition for solar energy, on which their lives depend. Once believed to be a ruthless and unbridled battle, more recent study of this struggle for existence suggests that cooperation and interdependence may be more important for the survival of a species than a no-quarter war.

1. A dragonfly, one of the chief predators among flying insects, pauses on a hibiscus bud in its ceaseless quest for prey.

2. A butterfly making the rounds of nearby flowers in search of nectar is seized by the dragonfly, to be devoured in mid-air.

3. Predator becomes prey with the snap of a bullfrog's jaws on the dragonfly. A tremendous user of energy, the dragonfly

How a Food Chain May Begin

This remarkable series of photographs, taken at the Weeki Wachee River in Florida, shows a typical marsh-community food chain. Beginning with the attack of a dragonfly on a nectar-sipping swallowtail butterfly (*above*), the chain moves through a series of ever-larger carnivorous animals. Each takes its turn in the double role of predator and prey, until

the chain ends (*following pages*) with a small hawk.

Food chains such as these are among the most fundamental relationships between plants and animals. To get a sufficient supply of food, and to keep from being eaten themselves, animals not only use an astonishing variety of adaptations but also cooperative partnerships like those involved in commen-

can eat its own weight in 30 minutes. The frog, more sedentary, could subsist longer on his meal—but his turn is next.

salism, mutualism and parasitism. The food chain itself, in any given instance, is the product of the plants and animals in the habitat, as well as their arrangement in a number of ecological niches. The frog in his niche can successfully ambush the dragonfly; but to see how his camouflage may sometimes fail to ensure his own survival, turn the page.

FOR THE NEXT STAGE—FROG VERSUS SNAKE—SEE NEXT PAGE

4. Ambushed himself, the startled frog is seized by a water snake before he can leap away. The snake, which will now devour the frog whole, is benefiting from five links that precede it in the food chain—frog, dragonfly, butterfly, flower and

Where a Food Chain Ends

In the life-and-death contest of a food chain only one animal, in the long run, can consistently emerge victorious—the predator who ends the entire chain; who knows no other predator that preys on him. The frog which here falls victim to the snake; the snake which is in turn devoured by the hawk—these are mere competitors in the unending struggle for light, water, minerals—in short, food—that begins with the lowliest plants. But the hawk, like the shark or the lion, is an ultimate consumer: he is a king.

Below him, competition sorts out all the plants and animals into their niches, even multiplying the number of niches available to them. And the food chains link and even branch—for some organisms,

5. But before the day is out the snake becomes prey for the hawk which, spotting it on the sand, swoops down to pick it up.

photosynthetic energy derived by plants from the sun—and a meal of this size will give it a day's supply of food and energy.

6. After a short tussle, the hawk flies off with the snake. Here the food chain ends, since the hawk has no predator but man.

such as the butterflies and moths, are parts of separate food chains during different phases of their life cycles. Others may shift because of the changing seasons, like the brown bear which feasts on the salmon as they migrate to spring spawning grounds, but has a vegetarian diet of berries in the autumn. Hibernation and migration, too, may set an end to a food chain like the one seen here. By the first frost the adult dragonfly is dead, the frog becomes dormant in the muddy bottom of the river, the snake is hibernating in a snug burrow and the warm-blooded hawk, the only member of this food chain which remains active all year round, will be the ultimate consumer of an entirely separate food chain.

Parasites as Predators

The difference between a carnivore and a parasite, a noted ecologist once remarked, is much like the difference between a burglar and a blackmailer. Most carnivores destroy and devour their prey all at once by superior size and strength. Parasites cannot afford such a direct approach—they must strike a subtle balance between the slow stealing of nourishment from their host and the continued health of that same host on whose well-being they depend.

One result of this is that parasites, so as not to harm their hosts unduly, must always remain much smaller. The parasites of a frog, for example, may

ECTOPARASITES

Living on the outside of their hosts, ectoparasites may move away from them for short periods and even spend part of their lives elsewhere. Some of the forms seen at the right, such as the tick and the leech, leave their hosts once they are gorged with blood. The orange mite stays longer, waiting for its host fly to lay eggs, which it will then consume. The nits and Lysiphlebus will remain long enough to reproduce and deposit eggs of their own.

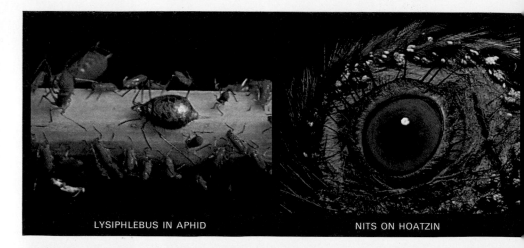

LYSIPHLEBUS IN APHID

NITS ON HOATZIN

PLANT PARASITES

Plant parasites depend both on other plants and on animals as hosts. Some, like the mistletoe, can supply part of their food by photosynthesis, but rely on their hosts for water and minerals. The dodder, with almost no photosynthesizing ability is entirely dependent on its host for nourishment. The witchweed looks like an independent green plant, but taps its hosts' roots for food and water, and the fungus gets food by attacking an ant host.

MISTLETOE ON OAK

DODDER ON CLOVER

ENDOPARASITES

Living inside of their hosts, endoparasites receive food and shelter. Secure from the problems of the outside world, they have little need for sensory organs, and hence have lost most of them. The sporozoa and the nematode parasitize the earthworm and the burrfish. The other three parasitize humans and infect them with disease: the liver fluke with bilharziasis, the flagellate with sleeping sickness, while the worm gives them trichinosis.

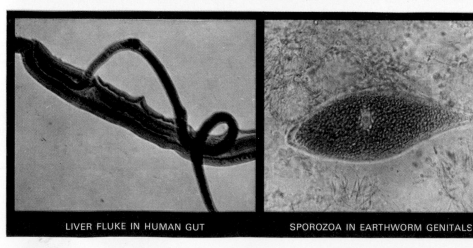

LIVER FLUKE IN HUMAN GUT

SPOROZOA IN EARTHWORM GENITALS

be 500 to 5,000 times as small as the frog itself. Even if parasites stay small and thereby keep their hosts from dying too quickly, they must have ways of getting to a new host if the old one dies. Most of the parasites that live on the outer surface of their hosts have kept their legs or wings and can move about freely when necessary. But those that live inside their hosts have often lost this independence. Instead, like the sleeping-sickness flagellate or the trichinosis worm (*below*), they have evolved elaborate life cycles which take them from one host to another as they progress from egg to adult.

ORANGE MITE ON FLY

TICK ON FENCE LIZARD

LEECHES ON LEECH

WITCHWEED ON CORN

MISTLETOE ON JUNIPER

FUNGUS ON ANT

NEMATODE IN FISH GUT

FLAGELLATE IN HUMAN BLOOD CELL

WORM CYST IN HUMAN MUSCLE

CAMOUFLAGED BY A SEA ANEMONE THAT CLINGS TO THE ROOF OF ITS BORROWED SNAIL-SHELL HOME, A HERMIT CRAB PEERS OUT OF ITS DOORWAY

HITCHING A RIDE, the immobile barnacles that cling to the tough and leathery hide of a humpbacked whale reap the benefits of being carried to constantly changing sources of food. This is a typically commensal association—one-sided in that it aids the barnacle but neither helps nor hurts the big whale.

COOPERATION PAYS OFF FOR THE SEA ANEMONE, DAMSELFISH AND SHRIMP, AS THEY HELP EACH OTHER TO GET FOOD, SHELTER AND SAFETY

The Rewards of Cooperation

When a barnacle gets a free ride on a whale, as shown at left, it gains from a cooperative relationship less harmful to its host than parasitism. This is called commensalism, and it is fairly low on a scale of cooperative relationships, increasing in intimacy, usually called symbiotic.

Somewhat more intimate is a mutualistic relationship, in which the two partners help each other, like the damselfish and sea anemone shown above. The flamboyant fish lure victims close to the anemone's lethal barbs, to which they are mysteriously immune. According to one theory, the damselfish is safe because it has been nibbling on the tentacles —in effect, getting small doses of the poison and thus gaining immunity.

Even more mysterious is the way the tiny fish seems able to direct the anemone's behavior. After the female has laid eggs at the base of the anemone, the male rubs against the tentacles and causes them to bend over, hiding the eggs. It may also maneuver the tentacles into removing its parasites, a job perhaps also done by the shrimp seen above.

113

A VELVETY SOLDIER BEETLE is dusted by pollen as it crawls through the watermelon flower on which it feeds. Its covering of fine hairs makes it an effective agent of cross-pollination.

Sweet Food for a Mission

What is good for an animal may also at times help a plant—and vice versa—so it is not surprising that plants and animals, too, have their useful cooperative relationships. Mutualism between flowers and insects, for example, is basic to the reproduction of many kinds of plant species. The insects visit the plants to get food, the plants dust them with pollen, and the insects carry this from flower to flower on an unwitting mission of fertilization. Plants may attract insects by their sweet nectar, scent or color. Bees can distinguish between the white, yellow, violet and perhaps ultraviolet colors of their favorite flowers, and tropical hummingbirds are guided to their favorite flowers by the red color which advertises abundant nectar. Still other plants have special structures, like the wild sage that dusts a visiting insect with pollen by means of a trigger that pulls down a stamen. Plants also ensure pollination by their timing devices, which mysteriously synchronize time of flowering with insect habits.

AT THE LIP of a sticky cockle, a sphinx moth sucks up nectar from the flower's throat. The insect's long proboscis helps it to cross-pollinate tubular blossoms such as honeysuckles.

GREGARIOUS WHIRLIGIGS spend their lives in a clump on top of the water, but can dive under its surface to hunt or to escape enemies. These beetles illustrate the most primitive form of aggregation; they have not sought each other out, but drifted together passively. No individual has any special role in the group. They are equal, and their massed bodies protect them.

SIGNALING SUDDEN DANGER, PRONGHORNS WARN THEIR FELLOWS BY FLASHING THE PATCH OF WHITE HAIR THAT GROWS ON THEIR RUMPS

The Rise of Societies

At a low social level, animals of a single species often live together in large numbers which are called aggregations. This may have started with the tendency of one-celled organisms to move away from danger and toward conditions which favor their survival, leading to unorganized groupings in certain spots. At somewhat higher levels, aggregations of birds that flock, fishes that school and animals that graze in herds afford some protection from predators and make breeding more certain.

For a group to be more than an aggregation, it must be better organized. Its members must have clear and separate roles. The most widespread of such divisions is that into male and female for reproduction. And along with the sexual differentiation are often found corresponding differences in appearance, physiology and behavior as well.

The next step may be the arrangement of animals in a social hierarchy. Certain animals in a group tend to be more dominant than others; they assume leadership. They may be the most active in defending the group's territory, or the first to get food and desirable mates. Among birds this sequence which gives each individual a fixed place is called the pecking order. Once such an organization exists, the group is well on its way toward being a society.

WHITE-BACKED VULTURES here are first to find a carcass, but may not be first to feast. Because their beaks and claws are weak they must wait for a stronger bird, such as the redheaded stork seen at center above, to rip open the fresh hide. Even then they eat in the pecking order for which they have fought —dominant birds gorge first, the weaker ones await their turn.

117

Family Survival

Gathered closely in the most intimate of relationships—the family—the California sea lions shown here have evolved a high level of social behavior which in some measure ensures survival of their species. The 500-pound males land in advance of the rest of the herd to stake out their territories. When the females arrive a little later, each bull fights for his harem of five to 20 cows, which he defends vigorously for the rest of the breeding season. Pups are born early in the summer, one to a cow, after a 12-month gestation period. Like all mammals, they must be suckled by their mothers, and taught to

SOCIABLE SEA LIONS BASK IN THE SUN ON THE ROCKY ISLANDS OF THEIR BREEDING GROUNDS OFF THE CALIFORNIA COAST. DURING THE SUMMER

fend for themselves. They do not know how to swim when they are born, and probably learn by struggling through the surf to follow their mothers into the sea. Some will inevitably drown, some will be trampled to death in the crowded herd, but the majority will be able to swim off with the herd by fall.

More primitive families than those of the seals are found among many lower vertebrates, whose offspring receive little care. As parents stay longer with their young, family units become more stable and evolve toward the most complex groups of all —the societies of insects and the higher mammals.

THEY GATHER TO MATE AND GIVE BIRTH TO THEIR PUPS. BY AUTUMN, THE HERDS DEPART TO SPEND THE WINTER ANYWHERE FROM MEXICO TO ALASKA

A CONGOLESE LICHEN MANTID

A KENYA MANTID

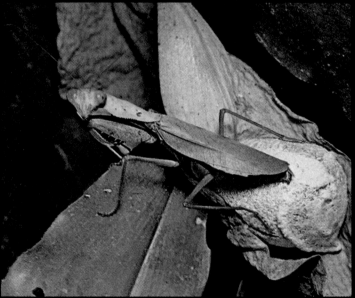

A MANTID FROM THE CONGO

A RHODESIAN MANTID

A PERUVIAN LEAF MANTID

A MADAGASCAR LEAF-LITTER MANTID

AN UNCANNY LIKENESS matches
mantids from many habitats to the
twigs and leaves on which they
live. Heightening the usefulness of
their disguise is a behavioral adaptation—the ability to stay still.

6

The Fit
and
the Unfit

CHARLES DARWIN concluded his monumental *The Origin of Species* with these
words: "There is grandeur in this view of life . . . having been originally
breathed by the Creator into a few forms or into one; and that, whilst this planet
has gone cycling on according to the fixed law of gravity, from so simple a beginning endless forms most beautiful and most wonderful have been, and are
being evolved." Grandeur is the only word for it; no one, contemplating the
nearly million and a half different kinds of plants and animals known to science,
can fail to be impressed, as Darwin was, by the wondrous variety of life—all of it
sprung from the humble beginnings of a few lowly forms.

How far that variety extends is not yet known. In the animal kingdom, almost
all the mammals, reptiles and amphibians that now populate the planet are believed to have already been discovered; there may be a few unrecorded species
lurking in remote spots, but the number is probably very low. By contrast, the
fishes that inhabit the ocean deeps are largely unknown, and there probably are
hundreds of thousands of insects and other invertebrates yet to be identified.

This enormous variety of life is not all evenly distributed over the globe. Although the seas cover more than 70 per cent of the earth's surface, their diversity

of living forms is much less than that of the land. This is partly because water offers a more uniform environment and partly because of the buoyancy of water itself, which makes it unnecessary for aquatic plants to develop the many varieties of supporting structures and photosynthetic and reproductive adaptations that are found in land plants. With a much greater diversity of plants on land, it follows that the animals that depend on them are offered a wide assortment of niches for shelter and feeding. Almost every tissue of almost every species of plant is consumed by one kind of animal or another. The greatest plant predators are the approximately 750,000 known species of insects, most of which have special adaptations to exploit some special kind of plant food.

All living things possess a tremendous biotic potential to reproduce their own kind at rates which, if allowed to go unchecked, would quickly flood their environments. As just one example, there is a single-celled animal, *Paramecium*, which divides in two when it is about 22 hours old. In another 22 hours, each of these two animals will have grown to full size and is ready to divide again, and so on. If a solitary *Paramecium* began to divide on January 1—and if all of its offspring survived—by March 7 its descendants would have a volume of a cubic mile. By April 12, their combined volume would be as large as that of the earth. Obviously no such population explosion could ever take place in nature—yet every species possesses a similar potential to grow and multiply fantastically. This inherent capacity to reproduce is limited by numerous factors such as starvation, accidents, drought and other hazards, including the activities of predators and parasites. Lumped together, these factors constitute what is known as "environmental resistance." To survive, every species of animal or plant must evolve a fitness to the world around it, allowing it to overcome the resistance of the environment—otherwise it would be known only as a fossil and not as a creature with whom man currently shares the globe.

THE concept of the adaptation of animals to their environment is deceptively simple: it means merely that any living thing is somehow fit to live where and how it actually does live. An adaptation is any feature that allows the organism to exist under the conditions imposed by its habitat—to make full use of the nutrients and energy, the heat and light available to the community, to obtain protection against enemies and the variations of climate. The mouth parts of various common fishes are good illustrations of how jaws and teeth may be adapted to different modes of feeding. Many fishes, such as trout, have strong, jutting, well-toothed jaws adapted for catching prey—others, like the seahorse, have mouths that are little more than pores through which food is strained. These are the obvious adaptations. Actually every creature is a bundle of adaptations, most of them exceedingly inconspicuous, that allow it to survive, reproduce and use the physical resources of the habitat effectively.

The different adaptations in different species probably arose through the action of the environment working as a sieve upon the accidental genetic variations every species undergoes. Although the individual plants of a species of grass growing in a meadow may all look very much alike, they do have genetic differences. These differences may be extremely slight, but they exist, and in some cases they may be sufficient to favor one plant over another in the struggle to maintain itself among its neighboring grass plants in that particular meadow. This is where the "sieve" effect of the environment comes in; the plants that vary too much from the optimum are strained out—they die or do not reproduce themselves. Nevertheless, slight genetic differences persist from generation to generation, and what might be called a tug of war is continually going on between the diversity of the genes, pulling the species in the direction of a diversity of types, and the restraining hand of the environment, acting always to pull it back to "normal." The consequence, in the plant's traditional environment, is a group of individuals that seem virtually identical. But move the plants to a quite different environment, and most of them will perish. A few, however, that possess a slightly different genetic pattern will tend to produce a kind of plant that is different too—"normal" for the new environment. When these useful variations that allowed the plant to survive in a new environment are passed on successfully to a species' descendants, they become beneficial adaptations.

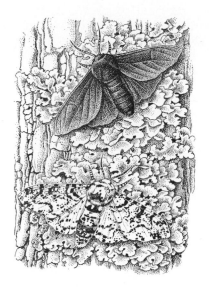

Planting a field in an arid climate with wheat from an area of high rainfall will result in a field mostly of dead plants; but a few plants with an accidental adaptation to drought will not be strained out and will result in a new variety of drought-resistant wheat. Many of man's crops and ornamental plants have been bred by this method of selecting survivors with beneficial adaptations. Not always, however, are the responses completely beneficial. A striking case is the barrel cactus of the desert, which usually germinates in the shade of a low shrub; but as it grows it leans in the direction of the brighter light, to such an extent that it eventually topples over and dies. Before that happens, though, it has usually flowered and set seed, thus ensuring the survival of the species.

Among the bundles of adaptations that make up any species, a universal one is the very ability to adapt. The fresh-water *Paramecium* can be killed promptly by suddenly adding a large amount of salt to its water. However, if the salt is added gradually, the *Paramecium* becomes adapted to the salt in its new environment, and the amount needed to kill it becomes greater and greater. Man, too, is able to habituate himself to toxic drugs, such as arsenic, by taking small but increasing doses. A human transplanted from sea level to a mountaintop will usually experience severe breathing difficulties in the rarefied atmosphere, but in a short time his body will adapt by increasing the number of red blood cells, and hence the oxygen-carrying capacity of his blood. Animals, including man, adapt to a foreign and sometimes disease-causing substance by producing a specific antibody that inactivates it.

There are generally three kinds of adaptations—structural, physiological and behavioral. Examples of structural adaptations are found in the great diversity in the feet and bills of birds or in the accordion-pleated storage reservoir of the saguaro cactus that allows it to conserve water for times of shortage. Almost everyone is aware that some animals are camouflaged from enemies by a variety of shapes and colors: the walking stick insects, which are thin and attenuated, with what appear to be little nodes on their bodies, thus making them closely resemble twigs; the willow ptarmigan, which changes the colors of its feathers from winter white to summer brown and thus matches the changing seasons. Other kinds of animals not only lack camouflage, but also actually appear to go out of their way to call attention to themselves; their striking coloration is a warning to advertise that they are unpalatable or dangerous and should be left alone. The brightly spotted ladybird beetle has a noxious taste to predators; the yellow-and-black wasp has a sting; a rattlesnake uses not color but sound to warn away large mammals that might tread on it. In the endless adaptations of living things, still other animals have taken to mimicry; these frauds have no unpleasant taste nor are they equipped with armament—they gain protection because they are mistaken for the warning-colored species.

THE CASE OF THE PEPPERED MOTH

England's Industrial Revolution has produced a most striking example of natural selection due to environment change —the peppered moth. Before 1850, it was known as a pale moth, well camouflaged against the light lichen covering trees. But when industrial soot and smoke began to coat the trees with grime, the pale forms were largely replaced by dark ones, better concealed from predators in the blackened countryside. Within only decades, the once-abundant pale form became rare except in rural areas.

A variation of adaptive coloration is found among birds that escape the duties of rearing their own young by laying their eggs in the nests of other species. Birds belonging to five different families around the world have adopted this method of nest parasitism, but one of the most highly evolved practitioners is the European cuckoo. Various races of the cuckoo lay their eggs in the nests of more than 125 other species of birds. But the imposition works only when the cuckoo's eggs resemble those of the host closely enough to deceive it—for many kinds of birds react to a strange object in the nest by rolling it out. The many races of the European cuckoo have indeed become adapted to mimicking the eggs of their favorite dupes. A Finnish race lays bright-blue eggs, primarily in the nests of redstarts and winchats, both of which also lay blue eggs. In Hungary, cuckoos lay greenish eggs blotched with brown and black—and so does their chief host, the great reed warbler. It is not only the color of the eggs that is adaptive, but also their size. Although cuckoos are large birds, they generally parasitize smaller ones; in these cases, the eggs of the cuckoo are small like those of their hosts. But cuckoos that parasitize large birds such as crows lay large eggs that match those of the host.

I N contrast to the obvious external adaptations that allow species to inhabit various environments, a second kind—the physiological—consists of unseen but ever-present internal modifications. A shipworm, which bores into the wooden pilings of wharfs, can exploit this unusual environment because its digestive system possesses something that is lacking in most other animals: a special enzyme that digests wood. The kangaroo rat of the southwestern deserts can live out its life without drinking a drop of water, surviving exclusively on seeds with a water content of less than 10 per cent; its physiological adaptation to arid conditions has resulted in a metabolism that greatly economizes this small amount of water. The llama, vicuña and viscacha—mammals that live as high as 15,000 feet in the Peruvian Andes—have hemoglobin with a much greater oxygen capacity than that of mammals living at lower altitudes where the oxygen content of the air is greater.

A third kind of adaptation is behavioral—and it is this that makes so many animals so endlessly fascinating. A species of moth with banded wings rests during the day on the banded leaves of a lily plant. The bands of the moth are a structural adaptation—but what the moth does with them is a behavioral adaptation. The moth always comes to rest so that its crossbands are parallel to the vertical bands of the leaf, thus giving the insect a high degree of concealment. All mammals are "warm-blooded"—that is, they can keep their internal body temperature approximately constant—but some, like the three-toed sloth of Central and South America, and the bat, are imperfectly so. The sloth solves the problems of overheating or freezing by living only in equatorial forests where nearly constant temperatures prevail; the bats migrate from cold areas to warm or they take refuge in caves and attics to hibernate.

The workings of these three primary types of adaptation are demonstrated with particular clarity by animals that inhabit the snowy northern portion of the hemisphere. To most people, snow is a uniform whiteness that lies like a blanket upon the land. But animals that inhabit areas where snow may persist for nine months of the year have many different kinds of snow to contend with —soft or crusted, deep or hard-packed—and so they have evolved different adaptations in structure, physiology or behavior. The winter distribution of the caribou is now believed to be partially a behavioral adaptation to the character

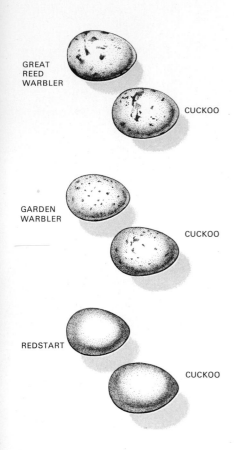

GREAT
REED
WARBLER

CUCKOO

GARDEN
WARBLER

CUCKOO

REDSTART

CUCKOO

THREE CUCKOO COPIES

Parasitic egg layers are birds with a particular problem: their way of life demands that others hatch their eggs. The various races of the European cuckoo have gone so far in perfecting deception that they can parasitize over 125 other species of birds. Shown here are three examples—the cuckoo's egg is usually slightly larger, but otherwise so good a copy that the host mother cannot tell the alien egg from her own. And when it hatches, she will feed the cuckoo chick.

of the snow cover. Most caribou abandon the wind-driven snow cover of the tundra in early autumn and migrate southward to the boreal forest. The caribou do not concentrate just anywhere in the tree zone, but find a location where the snow is soft, light and thin, permitting them to dig through it easily to uncover the food plants hidden below. These areas are usually invisible islands in a sea of snow that is less soft and fluffy. During the course of a winter, the snow islands shift, making new food sources available, and so do the caribou—which may account in part at least for the seemingly erratic wintertime movements of the herds.

Other northern mammals have structural rather than behavioral adaptations to the snow cover. The moose is equipped with long legs that serve as stilts reaching downward through deep snow to the firm ground beneath. A different structure for traveling through snow is one that allows the animal to go on top of it, best illustrated by the very large feet of the snowshoe hare. More generally the whole physiology of northern mammals is usually adapted to the cold. As a rule, individuals are larger than they would be if they lived in warmer climates, for bigger bodies are better conservers of heat than small ones, their ratio of body volume to skin surface being higher. Large body size and dense, insulating coats of fur allow many northern mammals—hares, wolves, moose, foxes and others—to remain active throughout the year despite the cold.

As ecologists learn more about the subtle behavioral and bodily adjustments animals make to the world of snow, a clue begins to emerge that might account for the wholesale extinction of certain northern mammals—the mammoth, mastodon, woolly rhinoceros, Irish elk and others—during the last glacial age. These mammals were no doubt adapted to cold dry environments with little snow. They may have lacked adaptations to the conditions of deep soft snow that occurred during the last glacial age. As the deep snows spread, these mammals may have tried to retreat or they may have become trapped here and there in snowless islands of still suitable environment, but which were destined to be slowly engulfed by the ever-encroaching blanket of white.

The great diversity of adaptations that can be evolved by a single group of related animals is exemplified by the marine worms, which have taken advantage of the wide spectrum of microhabitats found along a muddy shore. Even a cursory examination of worms taken from the zone between low and high tide reveals the numerous ways in which they have diverged from the generalized wormlike shape. A marine worm that travels on the surface of the wet mud has elaborate sensory equipment at its front end and well-developed side appendages. But one that burrows into the mud, where a protruding structure might be a handicap, has a simple head and scarcely visible appendages. Some of the burrowing worms do not actively forage for food, but construct tubes where they lie in wait for the food particles to come to them. They have no need for fancy sense organs; instead they are equipped with complex food-gathering organs, such as filters, mucus-secreting membranes, hairy surfaces or even graceful tentacles. One of the commonest of the marine worms—the bloodworm, often used by fishermen for bait—possesses an elephantlike proboscis which pulls the worm through the mud. When the proboscis is not being used for locomotion, it serves with its four large jaws as a food-gathering device. The unusually bright-red color of the bloodworms is due to hemoglobin in their blood. It is the same substance that is found in human blood and it helps them breathe in the oxygen-poor environment of mud.

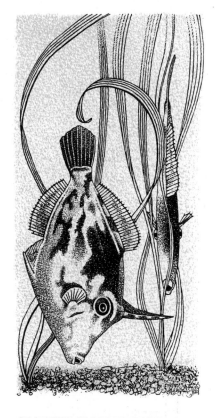

SEAWEED MASQUERADE

Like the moth with banded wings, the filefish shown above is doubly adapted for protection—structurally and in its behavior. It can change color to match its sea-surroundings. Near vegetation, the filefish takes an upside-down stance and gently waves its fins. With its undulating motions and cryptic coloration, the fish looks, to any would-be predators, like a seaweed frond or an eelgrass blade. For further protection, its flesh is permeated with poisonous alkaloids.

Most people naturally assume that the multitude of living things crammed into a rich environment—such as the teeming shore or the rain forest—must represent competition of the fiercest sort, but this is not true. Actually, diversity reduces competition and assures that many more individuals can live together in the same habitat. Two specialized creatures, each skilled in extracting energy in a different way from a particular niche of the environment, will do better than a single species that is a Jack-of-all-trades. Since they are more successful, they produce more total offspring than the generalized species could and eventually crowd it out. In a stable habitat, the specialized animal has obvious advantages over the generalized feeder, which meets competition wherever it turns. Furthermore, specialists can proliferate even further into a diversity of subspecialists that inhabit even narrower niches without increasing the severity of the competition—until, of course, the niches become so restricted that it is no longer possible to subdivide them.

The specialist, however, pays a penalty for its success. Even minor fluctuations in the environment may cause its extinction, while not seriously affecting the generalized animal, which can switch over to another form of food or another way of life. Thus, in disturbed habitats, it is often the nonspecialist that is most likely to endure, whereas in undisturbed habitats the nonspecialist usually loses out to the specialists. Furthermore, the greater its degree of specialization, the less ability an animal has to adapt further. An animal that is a specialist in a particular way of life may be much rarer than an animal only generally adapted to a wider environment—as is seen in certain species of ants that have developed the remarkable adaptation of enslaving other ant species. Not only are the slave makers much rarer than their enslaved species, but some of them have become so specialized that they starve to death even in the presence of abundant food if they are deprived of slaves to feed them and take care of the nest.

As one travels around the planet, it soon becomes apparent that numerous plants and animals from different parts of the world look alike, not because they are related, but because they have become adapted to the same ecological conditions. The evolutionary development of resemblances between unrelated organisms inhabiting similar environments is known as "convergence." Cacti, for example, are extraordinarily abundant in some New World deserts, but they are unknown in Africa. Instead, African deserts are populated by euphorbias, which look enough like cacti to be sometimes mistaken for them by hothouse growers. Cacti and euphorbias are both succulent, spiny, flowering plants adapted to arid conditions—but actually euphorbias belong to an entirely different family of plants, the spurges, none of which has the slightest true resemblance to cacti. Even though these two groups of plants are similar in their adaptations to a desert environment—including the development of waterstoring devices and of spines instead of flat leaves—they have still retained their ancestral characteristics, especially their reproductive structures. There are equally striking examples of unrelated look-alikes among animals. The jack rabbit is an abundant animal in the North American grasslands, but in similar grasslands of the Argentine pampas there are no jack rabbits; instead, the jack rabbit niche is filled by the cavy. This creature has long hind legs, big ears and behaves much like a North American jack rabbit, but is actually a relative of the guinea pig. The pronghorn antelope, an exclusively North American species of the grasslands, has its counterpart in the saiga antelope of Eurasia and a great variety of African antelopes, none of which are related to the pronghorn.

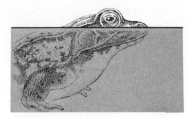

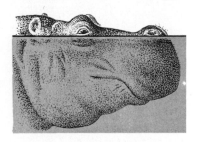

THREE SIGNIFICANT PROFILES

What do frogs, crocodiles and hippopotamuses have in common? The first is an amphibian, the second a reptile, the third a mammal—but all three breathe air and live in water. Hence they all have nostrils and eyes that protrude above the surface while their bodies are submerged: another example of convergent evolution.

Convergent adaptation can be seen clearly in an environment that places special demands upon its inhabitants. The devices by which the dwellers in a rushing mountain stream manage to live in the fast currents are often similar, although the animals using them belong to widely separate groups. Flatworms, leeches, snails, water mites, larvae of numerous insects—all invertebrates, but otherwise only distantly related to each other—have become similarly streamlined. Their bodies tend to be shield-shaped or circular; their upper surfaces are smooth and without protrusions. Organs of attachment that work by suction are common among unrelated stream species. Leeches possess suction cups, as do the larvae of a number of different kinds of insects; some tadpoles and fishes (such as the armored catfish of South America) have their mouth parts, lower surfaces and even fins modified into sucking apparatuses that help them maintain their position in the fast-flowing water.

THE worldwide examples of convergent adaptations are indeed numerous. Aquatic mammals and birds have both independently evolved blubber for insulation against the cold, as can be seen in whales, seals and penguins. And, of course, whales resemble fishes in their streamlined shape. The mantis shrimp, a crustacean, has forelimbs similar to those possessed by the praying mantis, an insect. Many unrelated animals—such as the armadillo (a mammal), the pill bug (an isopod), some mites (arachnids) and beetles (insects)—can roll themselves into a ball and in that way not only protect themselves from predators, but also conserve moisture in a dry habitat. That this is an ancient adaptation is proved by the fact that the same thing could be done by trilobites, which became extinct some 250 million years ago. Mammals that feed on a particular food tend to develop the same kinds of adaptations, although they may belong to completely different groups. The spiny anteater, banded anteater, New World anteater, aardvark and pangolin are distantly related mammals from four continents. All feed on ants and termites and all have cylindrical tongues, inconspicuous teeth and extended faces. With the sole exception of the banded anteater, they all have feet adapted for digging into the nests of these insects.

Convergence has reached its greatest extent on the island continent of Australia, where almost all of the ecological roles of life filled on other continents by placental mammals are filled solely by marsupials (pouched mammals, such as the New World opossum). If there had been a land bridge connecting Australia with the Oriental realm during the early Age of Mammals, there undoubtedly would have been a mixture of placentals and marsupials; but instead, Australia became isolated before the placental mammals developed in Asia. The isolated marsupials spread over highly varied environments; they diversified rapidly, becoming specialists in many niches that are occupied by placental mammals in the rest of the world. The Tasmanian "wolf," for example, is not a wolf at all but a marsupial that much resembles a Northern Hemisphere wolf in appearance as well as in its habit of running down prey. Although it has these resemblances to the Eurasian and North American wolves, it possesses many other, more subtle resemblances to kangaroos, with which it is grouped in zoological classification. Australia also possesses marsupials that resemble mice, cats, moles, sloths, squirrels, groundhogs and other common placental mammals that fill similar ecological niches on other continents.

There are three famous rules (or rather generalizations, since many exceptions exist) that apply to adaptations of warm-blooded animals. Within any one species, (1) the average size of individuals is smaller in warm climates and

TOOLACHE WALLABY

SCRUB WALLABY

"RAT" KANGAROO

TREE KANGAROO

ROCK WALLABY

ADAPTIVE RADIATION

All five of the Australian marsupials shown above stem from a common ancestor—they are all kangaroos. Their differences are the result of adaptive radiation—each is adapted to a separate ecological niche. Thus the toolache (now extinct because of man's predation) favored open grassland. The scrub wallaby prefers dense scrub for shelter and feeds on grassy patches. The more primitive "rat" kangaroo searches jungle litter for insects. The tree kangaroo and rock wallaby, living climbing lives, have evolved clinging, nonslip pads on their feet, and brush-tipped tails that act as rudders.

larger in cold climates (Bergmann's rule); (2) protruding body parts are shorter in colder than in warmer climates (Allen's rule); and (3) colors of animals tend to be darker in warm, moist climates and lighter in cold dry climates (Gloger's rule). These laws governing adaptations of mammals apply equally as well to man. The pigmentation of the races of man that inhabit the humid tropics follow Gloger's rule: everyone knows that the dark-skinned peoples who have historically concentrated around the equatorial regions—central Africa, southern Asia, Melanesia, northern Australia—do not sunburn as severely as whites nor are they as susceptible to skin cancer. The skins of white people lack the pigment melanin, which absorbs ultra-violet rays from the sun before they reach the sensitive portions of the skin, expelling the rays in the form of heat.

Prominent body parts such as long noses and limbs are reduced in the compact bodies of the Mongoloid race that arose in the cold of central Asia—which conforms to Allen's rule. The Mongoloid Eskimos can endure cold because their bodies burn more oxygen and produce more calories than the bodies of white men; the hand of an Alaskan Indian is kept warm by twice the flow of blood as is the hand of a white man. The application to man of the other part of Allen's rule is seen in the dark-skinned tribes that live in subtropical and tropical savannahs; they have elongated arms and legs that aid in dissipating heat. In conforming to Allen's rule, the races of man even demonstrate convergent adaptation. The Lapps of northern Scandinavia have been shown, by the careful study of their blood groups, facial proportions and other factors, to be a Caucasoid race—yet they resemble the Mongoloids that inhabit similar cold climates. Finally, the races of man are seen to conform to Bergmann's rule by the example of the pygmies and other dwarfed peoples that inhabit warm climates, and the tall Scandinavians that live in cold climates.

ALTHOUGH there are many differences among the different races, man as a whole has not displayed adaptive radiation as have the marsupials of Australia, nor has he ever developed such cumbersome features as the camel's hump or the anteater's extended face. One reason is that man is an evolutionary newcomer on the planet, and there simply has not been enough time for him to do this. Although there is great disagreement about the age of man, it is probably about a million years—and in that time he does not appear to have evolved any major modifications, except for somewhat straightening his vertical posture and showing an increasing tendency, in all races, toward round-headedness. But it also appears that man is a unique animal. He has specialized in *not* being a specialist. Since he can occupy more ecological niches than are known for any other species of animal—living in climates from the Arctic to the tropics, eating diets that range from almost pure vegetarian to almost exclusively meat—he obviously has not had to divide into several species to fill various niches. The dog, the first domesticated animal, is probably the only other creature that has so remarkable a range of forms while still remaining a single species.

Instead of blindly groping through the byways of natural selection, slowly gaining adaptations that are tested by passing through the sieve of the environment, man has been able to manufacture his own adaptations—fire, clothing, tools—*outside* of his own body instead of as parts of it. This has given man powers never held by any other form of life. Whether those powers will be used to maintain the delicate ecological relationships that have slowly developed over these past billion or so years of life—or whether they will be used to rip apart the elaborate tapestry of life—man himself must determine.

A DISPOSABLE AZURE TAIL WHICH BREAKS OFF UNDER ATTACK DISTRACTS THE ENEMIES OF THE SKINK FROM THE VITAL ORGANS IN ITS TRUNK

Secrets of Success

The measure of success in the natural world is the survival of a species. In the history of life, survival has not been the general rule—about one third of the 2,500 animal families known from the fossil record are still alive today. Their persistence speaks for the perfection of their adaptations—and also, as shown on following pages, their ability to keep up with changes in their surroundings.

129

FITTED TO A NOCTURNAL, ARBOREAL LIFE, THE FLYING SQUIRREL'S ROUND, LARGE-PUPILED EYES COLLECT DIM LIGHT TO AID KEEN NOSE AND EARS

The Best Way to Survive

More than 1.3 million separate species of plants and animals populate the earth today, each inhabiting its own niche in the environment, each better adapted to exploit that niche than any other. And one way of looking at this huge diversity of living creatures is to study, as ecologists do, the marvelous interrelationships with their environment and each other, reflected by their modes of life.

To the casual eye, all living forms may seem to be simply haphazard bundles of adaptations, evolved to fit a situation they blundered into; but on closer examination, the concept of adaptation may further an understanding of life. For if life is to persist, an organism must secure the food and energy it needs to survive where it lives, and must be able to reproduce. Adaptation thus may be defined as the way a plant or animal is organized in its structure, physiology and behavior to carry out these goals.

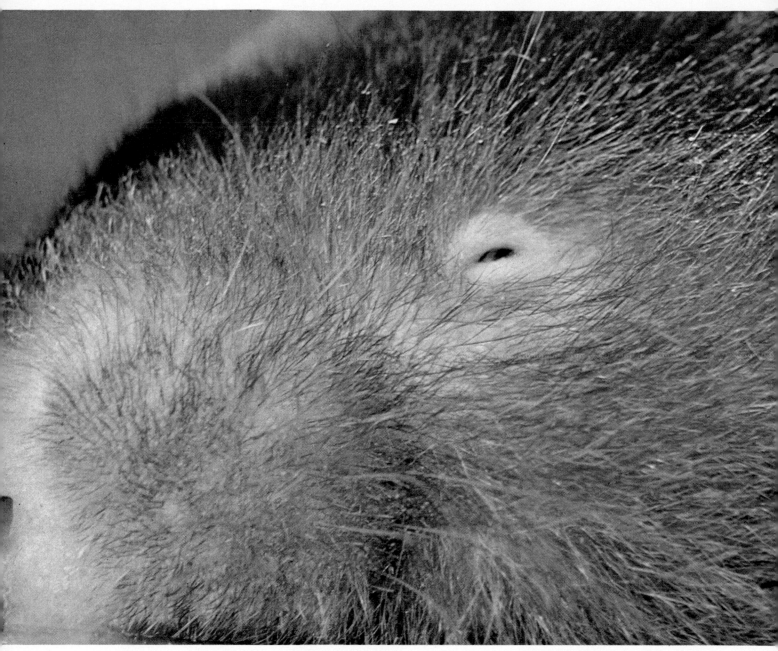

THE MOLE RAT, BY CONTRAST, LIVING UNDERGROUND, NEEDS ONLY A SLIT FOR ITS FEEBLE EYES, WHICH CAN BARELY TELL DAY FROM NIGHT

In the framework of evolutionary theory adaptation appears as a constant process of testing and rejecting—with the environment acting as the testing agent on the organisms which are evolving. Those organisms which adapt themselves best will survive to perpetuate themselves. But adaptations carried to the extreme sometimes lose their survival value. Some, like those of the dinosaur, led to a dead end. Some render the organism too inflexible in the face of change, like the ivory-billed woodpecker, which could not adjust when the vast areas of virgin forest it needed disappeared.

Finally, then, the most useful adaptation is neither the most astonishing structure nor the most rigidly patterned behavior, but rather adaptability itself—to light or darkness, treetop or burrow—and a capacity to alter ways of life as the environment is altered, by nature or the drastic acts of men.

Strange Traits Bred in Darkness

For students of evolution, caves are ideal natural laboratories in which to study adaptations. Not only do they offer an environment where heat and cold, humidity and light remain fixed throughout the year, but the unique conditions found in caves produce dramatically exaggerated effects on plant and animal populations. And from their entrances through a twilight zone extending as far back as light can penetrate to the region of perpetual night, they harbor a surprising number of habitats.

A partial cave dweller of the interior zone is the Venezuelan oilbird, or guacharo (*below*), the only bird known to live in caves. Though it roosts and nests in the sheltering cave, it finds its food outside—in nocturnal darkness. The guacharo's blue eyes can see, but in the dark the bird navigates effectively, like a bat, by bouncing echoes off objects in its path.

True cave dwellers like the other animals shown here never leave their dark dwellings, but spend their entire lives in blackness. In such surroundings, these animals show many similar traits, sharing certain features unknown in related forms in the outer world. There are, for instance, no large animals that are permanent residents in caves; rather cave creatures tend to be small and slender, with thin, pale body coverings. Surrounded by high humidity, they need no special hair or scales to hold or repel moisture. They have no use for eyes and hence have lost them, evolving instead long organs of touch and a sharp sense of smell for locating sparse food. Scavengers or hunters, they follow their own cycles, unrelated to day and night outside. But while most of these blind animals bear sightless progeny, young salamanders are born able to see. If their larvae are forcibly raised in the light, they retain their vision. Apparently even countless generations spent in caves have not yet produced a fixed trait of sightlessness that is inherited.

THE VENEZUELAN GUACHARO LIVES IN TWO WORLDS

AN OZARK CAVE SALAMANDER HAS SIGHTLESS EYES

THIS BLIND CRAYFISH LIVES BY FEEL

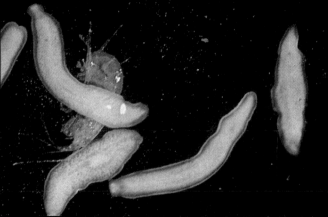

PALE CAVE FLATWORMS FEED ON AN AMPHIPOD

THIS RARE BLIND BEETLE SURVIVES ON SMALL FUNGI

THE CREAM-COLORED TYPHLITHYS OF KENTUCKY, LIKE OTHER CAVE FISHES, SELDOM GROWS MORE THAN THREE INCHES LONG

VERSATILE IN THE DESERT, the ocotillo bears fiery flowers and short leaves (*top*) during wet spells, but sheds them between rains (*bottom*) to conserve moisture for a new crop.

THE STRANGLER FIG germinates high on a tree, then snakes down its host by means of aerial roots. Thus it eventually preempts space in the sunlight formerly held by its strangled host.

The Problems of Staying Put

A fundamental difference between plants and animals is that while animals faced with difficult situations can go elsewhere, plants must stay rooted to the spot. Thus a successful plant must be truly well fitted to its surroundings—and indeed, some can withstand extremes. Some blue-green algae can tolerate heat of 185°F., some seeds survive at −460°F. Plants like the strangler fig at left fill a narrow niche; they grow only in tropical and subtropical forests, and only in a certain way. Others in a less competitive habitat, such as the desert, have bizarre adaptations to cope with special conditions of climate. Still others perform invisible physiological feats, like some alpine plants that transform solar energy into heat that melts the snow surrounding their shoots.

SPIKY THORNS of the honeylocust present a mystery. Most abundant on the trunk, they may be an effective barrier to keep small animals or even birds from climbing to the flowering crown. But cattle wait until the long green pods fall to the ground, and bobwhites eat the seeds when short of other food, thus foiling this possible function of the four-inch thorns.

How Grasslands Shape the Species

None of the animals pictured opposite are even cousins to each other—yet many look alike. Leapers, burrowers, climbers, runners, they are all inhabitants of grassland biomes throughout the world, and this explains their similarities. They are ecological equivalents, animals of different ancestry living under similar conditions, which have become similarly adapted by the process of convergent evolution.

Grassland, of course, occurs on all continents; once grasses even covered 42 per cent of the earth. The grasses which characterize this biome are perennials which continue to grow even after their tips have been eaten. This supports grazing mammals, and these have reached their greatest numbers here.

In every grassland—whether the North American plains and prairies, the South American pampas, Asian t'sao-yüan, African veld or Australian savanna—locomotion is one of the most important adaptations for survival because grazers are ideal prey for carnivores. Leaping over the tops of the grass enables such creatures as rabbits, jerboas and kangaroos to scan the horizon for danger. Burrowing makes use of another level—it offers concealment and reduces competition. Running is useful for pursuit or flight—and here, where there is only open land, are the fastest runners of the world.

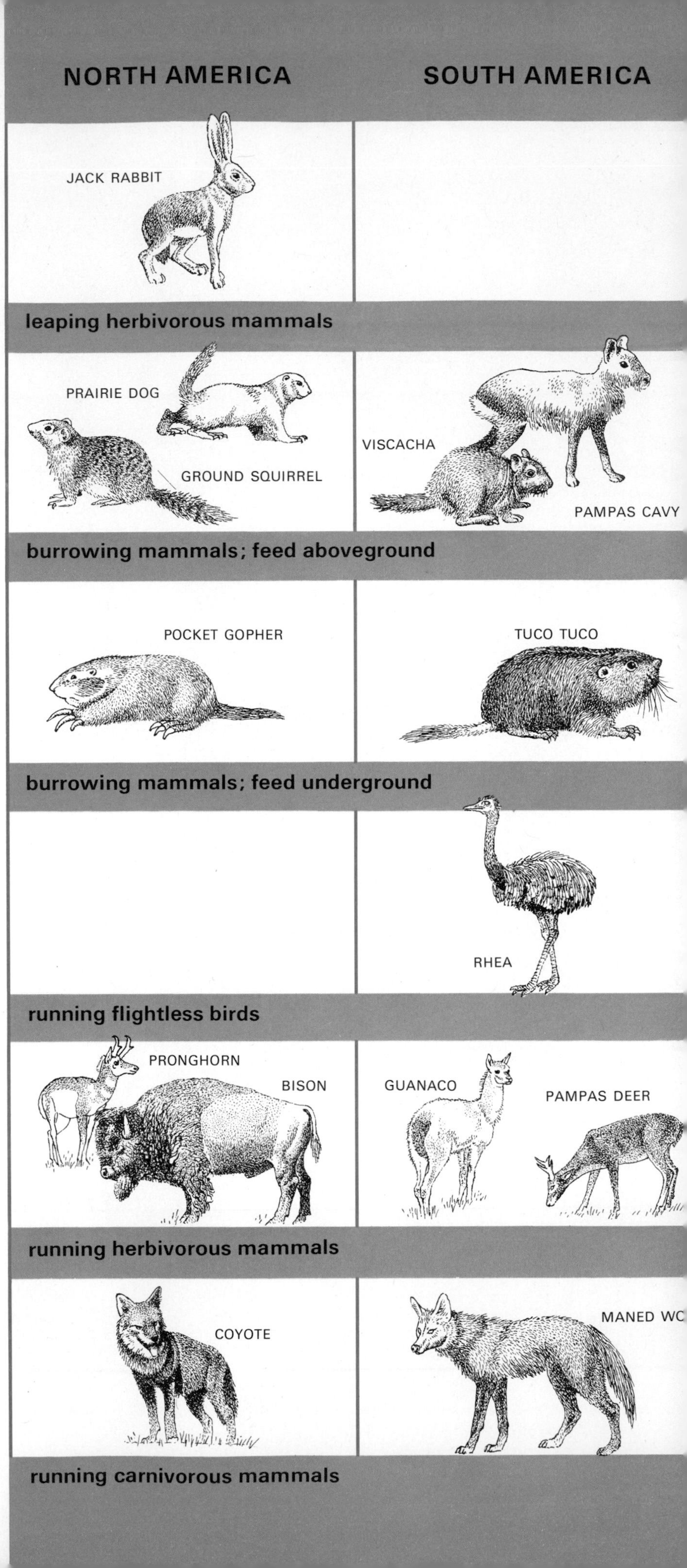

NORTH AMERICA	SOUTH AMERICA
JACK RABBIT	

leaping herbivorous mammals

| PRAIRIE DOG / GROUND SQUIRREL | VISCACHA / PAMPAS CAVY |

burrowing mammals; feed aboveground

| POCKET GOPHER | TUCO TUCO |

burrowing mammals; feed underground

| | RHEA |

running flightless birds

| PRONGHORN / BISON | GUANACO / PAMPAS DEER |

running herbivorous mammals

| COYOTE | MANED WO[LF] |

running carnivorous mammals

ASIA | AFRICA | AUSTRALIA

ASIATIC JERBOA | SPRINGHAAS | RED KANGAROO

HAMSTER | AFRICAN GROUND SQUIRREL | WOMBAT

"MOLE RAT" | GOLDEN MOLE | MARSUPIAL MOLE

OSTRICH | EMU

SAIGA | ZEBRA

WILD HORSE | SPRINGBOK

PALLAS CAT | CHEETAH | TASMANIAN "WOLF"

LION

A LION CUB GNAWS PLAYFULLY AT THE HARD SHELL OF A TORTOISE

Learning by Doing

How do the young of animals learn to use the various tools which evolution has given them for survival? The answer lies in their behavioral adaptions: instinct and learning. This year-old lion cub could not survive were it not fed by its mother. Although some day its sharp claws, strong limbs and powerful jaws will enable it to pull down an antelope or zebra, it does not even know what to hunt until its parents teach it. But it is adapted to hunt; the instinct is there, and meanwhile the cub may improve its coordination by seemingly random play with a handy object—in this case, a tortoise.

On its part, the tortoise is well adapted to emerge intact from this potentially lethal game. It has retracted its long, flexible neck, head and limbs into its shell. And the shell which covers its soft flesh is so tough an armor that turtles have survived almost unchanged for over 175 million years—some 174 million before the first lions showed up on earth.

FRUSTRATED after turning the tortoise in all directions, the cub finds no chink in its defense. An adult lion would never attempt such a task, unless it were starving.

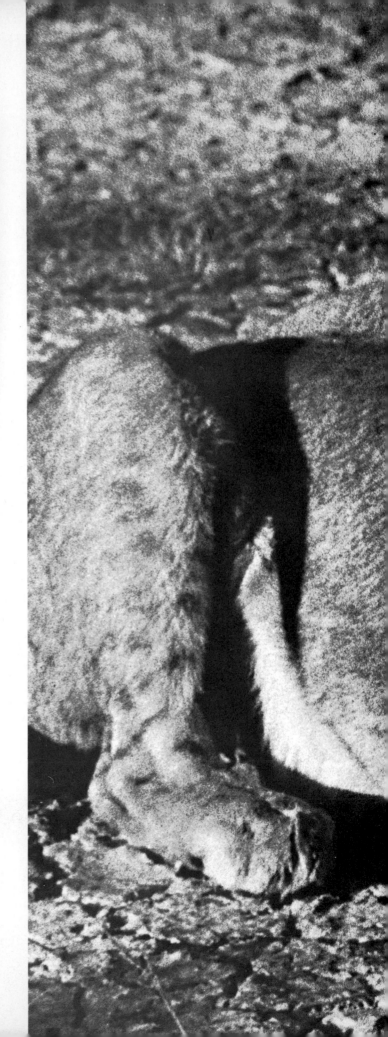

7

The Rise
and Fall
of Populations

BEHOLD," Moses warned Pharaoh, "thus saith the Lord God of the Hebrews: tomorrow will I bring the locusts into thy coast: and they shall cover the face of the earth, that one cannot be able to see the earth." Plagues of locusts, such as those visited upon Egypt, have long been a reality to desert peoples, and other dramatic assemblages of animals—the rats of Hamelin, the rabbits of Australia, the lemming hordes of Scandinavia—are legendary throughout the living world. Man has always stood in awe of the sudden exuberance of nature—of skies filled with birds during migrations, of streams suddenly choked with spawning salmon, of seas seemingly aflame at night with the sudden rise to the surface of endless numbers of microscopic animals. That life can take these remarkable upward surges is due to the constant fluctuations in the balance between species in the community and to the population changes within the species themselves. Sometimes changes are the result of seasonal or other cyclical influences; sometimes they are due to changes in the physical environment itself or in the often delicate balances between predators and prey; occasionally they are inexplicable.

Any group of organisms of the same species that occupies a given space at a particular moment in time is known as a population. There is a great difference between an individual and *a population* of individuals. An individual is born, ages and then dies; but to the ecologist these characteristics are meaningful only when they are applied to the many individuals inhabiting a particular locality—in short a population. Sometimes there are similarities in the populations of a species wherever the species occurs, but often a population at one place will differ markedly from those at other places nearby, even when apparently similar conditions prevail. Each population exhibits a number of measurable characteristics—a birth rate, mortality, density, a capacity for increase, as well as various complex relationships to its environment. Established populations have generally done so well in adapting to their environments—in exploiting the food resources and breeding sites, in coping with the various changes—that an invading alien, a hybrid or a mutant can find opportunity to take hold only in a disturbed area.

A NYONE who thinks about populations for a moment must be impressed by obvious differences in the numbers of individuals making up a population. There may be 50 trees of a particular species populating as large an area as an acre of forest—but there may be a million diatoms in a bucket of sea water. The density of the population in relation to the space that it occupies may exert considerable effect upon the community; a single crow in a hundred-acre cornfield would cause little damage, but a thousand crows descending upon those same hundred acres would wreak havoc. The abundance or scarcity of a population may fluctuate widely, but there are definite upper and lower limits to its density—determined by the energy flow in the community, restrictions of space and climate, the position of the organism in the fabric of the community, and the size and rate of metabolism of the organism itself. Competition, predation and other stabilizing factors of the environment hold the reins on population increase beyond a certain maximum. The average density of bobwhite quail populations differs widely between southern Georgia, a favorable climate for these birds, and unfavorable Wisconsin, at the edge of their range. In one study conducted over a number of years, the density of quail in Georgia was found to range between 20 and 100 birds per 100 acres—but in Wisconsin it averaged only 2.7 to 9.6 for the same amount of land. The effect of man may also be a factor in the density of a population. For example, the world population of gannets—large sea birds that nest in only 22 colonies along the shores of the North Atlantic—was about 171,000 breeding pairs in 1829. Sixty years later, after considerable persecution by man, the number had fallen to 54,000 pairs. But since then the birds have been protected and today the population has risen to some 143,000 breeding pairs.

The study of populations is particularly rewarding in the far north because of the paucity of resident species and the relative simplicity of the natural communities. A northern predator feeding upon a particular prey animal rarely has an alternative source of prey if its regular source fails—unlike temperate and tropical predators, which can pursue any one of many possible alternates. As a result the relationships between northern populations stand out clearly. One of the characteristics of northern populations is that they show regular and violent oscillations between abundance and scarcity—as has been learned from the careful records the Hudson's Bay Company of Canada has kept since about 1800 of pelts taken by trappers each year. These records show that in the tundra the number of foxes trapped annually moved up and down rhythmically, reaching a peak about every three to four years, followed by a rapid decline. Eventually it was discovered that the foxes' ups and downs were tied to those of the lemmings, practically their exclusive food source in the tundra. The lemmings, which have a high reproductive potential, build up to fantastic numbers (well known from their legendary marches to the sea), then suddenly die off and become scarce; it takes the few surviving lemmings about three to four years to reach their population peak once again.

In the northern coniferous biome, it was found that there are also cycles in the populations of the lynx and its principal prey, the snowshoe hare—but these had a rhythm of 9 to 10 years. So wide are these oscillations that in peak years the company has taken an average of 115,000 hare skins, compared with only 10,000 immediately after the population crash. As these cycles were more closely studied, it was learned that other inhabitants of the far north were also tied to them. Snowy owls follow the three-to-four-year lemming cycle, and after the rodents' precipitous decline they are forced to search elsewhere for food and often range as far south as Maryland. Other birds of prey, the great horned owl and the goshawk that inhabit the coniferous forest biome, also have population cycles connected to the 9-to-10-year hare cycle. The number of far northern species that undergo cycles is considerable. Oscillations in population are, in fact, both more evident and more prevalent in any harsh environment—not only in arctic areas, but also in deserts and at high altitudes.

Various attempts have been made to explain these cycles by the influence of sunspots, cosmic rays or disease epidemics, and the full explanation is obviously complex. It is generally agreed that in an environment of a simple food chain, based on a widespread but limited number of plant species, the primary consumers can increase rapidly and overcrowd their habitat; in the case of many primary consumers, this seems to take either 3 to 4 years or 9 to 10 years. Once the population reaches this high level, it endangers its own existence. It may simply eat itself out of a food supply and starve; it may fall prey to other animals that have similarly increased in response to the abundant new source of prey that has been presented to them, or it may decline suddenly due to the stress of overcrowding. In the case of snowshoe hares, it has been shown that stress causes their livers to degenerate, leaving an inadequate reserve of glycogen available for emergencies; under these conditions, sudden excitement or fear, instead of stimulating it to run, may cause a hare to go into convulsions, sink into a coma and die. Whatever the cause, the result is a sudden decline in the population of the primary consumer, followed by a crash in the population of the predators that depend upon it—and the beginning of a new cycle.

THE abundance of a population is determined first of all by its birth rate, and there is a tremendous difference between the potential rate and the rate actually realized. In the estuaries of rivers, the American oyster exhibits a startling birth potential: a single individual is capable of spawning more than 100 million eggs, although the actual hatching rate is much lower. Another estuarine animal, the sea catfish, by contrast has a very low birth potential. A single female rarely produces more than 30 eggs at a time—but the protection given them in the period of parental care, during which the male carries the eggs in his mouth until hatched, contributes to a very high actual birth rate.

Birds, too, provide interesting material for study. Recently, 170 nests containing eggs of 12 species of birds in a deciduous woodland of Indiana were closely observed throughout the breeding season. Exactly 598 eggs were laid in

THE HARE AND THE LYNX

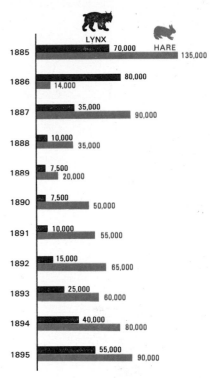

The 9- or 10-year rise and fall in the population of snowshoe hares is closely followed by the Canada lynx. When the hares have reached a peak, the lynxes, with abundant prey at hand, are still building up. Thus when the hares drop off because of overcrowding or disease, many lynxes also starve. With fewer predators and enough food for themselves, the hares again multiply. Graphs based on pelts handled by the Hudson's Bay Company show one cycle (above) and cycles repeated over eight decades (below).

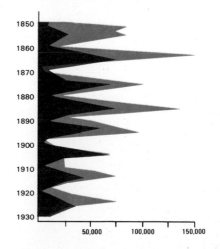

these nests, including 25 eggs of the parasitical cowbird, which does not build its own nest. But only 231 eggs—or 39 per cent—hatched. And of these 231 hatchlings, only 105 survived long enough to reach an age when they could fly from the nest. Almost all of the failures to produce young successfully were due to predation, particularly by snakes and small mammals, with fewer losses caused by parasites and unfavorable weather conditions. Naturally, many hazards still awaited these 105 young survivors, on their first flights, on their initial attempts at food getting, on their first migration, so that actually the number surviving to breed the following spring would be a mere handful compared to the nearly 600 eggs that were laid.

Often it is not reproductive potential alone that accounts for wide population fluctuations. Winds may sweep mosquitoes from exposed terrain and deposit them in unusual concentrations in sheltered places; the currents of lakes and oceans may similarly concentrate plankton. In addition to this kind of passive movement, there is the intentional congregation of many kinds of animals in a variety of situations. Some fishes travel in great schools; there are mass flights of waterfowl on migration; carrion feeders such as vultures or hyenas gather rapidly about a dead animal.

Birds of a feather do indeed flock together—for sociality is almost universal among birds of the same species. Everyone knows of the gregariousness of geese, ducks, herring gulls and most sea birds, but it is only in recent years that ornithologists have come to realize that there are less obvious aspects of social behavior among many kinds of birds. Although their theories are still controversial, a number of ecologists have now come to believe that even territoriality —once regarded as the epitome of antisociality, since it appears to keep birds apart—is a form of social behavior because it represents a respect for the rights of property and enables individuals to get along in fairly close proximity to one another. Territorial neighbors may be hostile to each other, but once territories have been determined, a neighbor does not kill off a neighbor or grab new territory. Territorial hostility serves simply to keep an individual from straying beyond its borders. These units of territory of a species population actually form a social network, complete with social conventions of aggressiveness, song or display, and protection of rights. The effect of territory is to create neighborhoods of individual families which own their households but which are bound socially to their next-door neighbors. The relations between next-door neighbors in birds are by no means utopian—but neither are they in human societies.

Most species of birds that are very numerous—a measure of ecological success—are unquestionably social. Probably the most numerous bird in the world is the Wilson's petrel, which nests in fantastic numbers on the Antarctic continent and on subantarctic islands. This species, like all the approximately 200 species of oceanic birds, is always social on its crowded breeding grounds. This might be thought to be the result of there being a limited number of areas suitable for nesting, but that is not so; there is usually an abundance of unoccupied breeding space that the petrels could use if they cared to. Clearly they prefer to be together, a universal condition among the birds that have conquered the most difficult of habitats for their kind, the sea. On land too, sociality and success go together; the 14 most numerous birds in England and Wales are all either obviously or subtly social.

There is still dispute among ornithologists about what biological benefits a population of birds might obtain through sociality. Many theories have been put forward and a number of them may indeed be perfectly correct, but not enough research has been carried out to support these theories with conclusive proof. It does seem, though, that the larger the breeding colony, the greater the visual and auditory stimulus to breed. There is a double benefit here. Not only do more adults breed, but they also seem to give their young better care, since a higher percentage of nestlings survives to the age when they can leave the nest. It has been reported that in order to establish a successful breeding colony of the guano-producing cormorant on its home islands off Peru, a minimum of 10,000 birds must build their nests at a density of about three nests per 10 square feet. The need for group stimulation is sometimes so great that in some sea bird species, such as gannets, it may account for unsuccessful breeding in small colonies. Another theory is that in unity there is obviously strength and protection against attacks by other birds or small predators; but on the other hand concentrations of eggs are particularly vulnerable to attack by man and other large predators.

THE flocking of birds at the feeding grounds does, however, ensure the full exploitation of a food crop. A flock of grazing geese is made to move steadily across a water meadow by the geese at the rear exerting pressure on those ahead. The geese in front are forced to move so fast that they leave food for the birds pushing at the rear. In the case of oceanic birds, their food of fishes and plankton is often distributed in clumps; a flock can detect and exploit these aggregations of prey more efficiently than can single individuals. Certain species, among them the little black cormorant and the white pelican, cooperate by fishing in formation, flying in large groups until they sight a shoal of fish. Then the lead birds settle on the water and concentrate the shoal by swimming in ever-narrowing circles. Some cormorants may even spread themselves across the mouth of a bay or river and drive the congested fish into shallow water, where they are more easily caught.

Birds are not the only social creatures. Animal aggregations are widespread throughout nature and they display all degrees of permanency, from a casual coming together for mating to the establishment of elaborate colonies that survive for years. Some insects—certain bees and wasps, all ants and termites—live in definite social organizations that are permanent and often extraordinarily intricate. Mammal herds, too, are usually permanent, their organizations outlasting the lives of the individual members. The herd has strong survival value. A single bison would probably succumb to a pack of wolves—but when in a group, the males form a circle with the young and females inside and in that way usually can ward off an attack. The wolf pack itself is an efficient social organization. A single wolf might have difficulty killing a deer, pronghorn or bison, but an organized pack can run down the prey animal in relays until it is exhausted. Some aggregations, on the other hand, are less permanent—they may last a year or as little as half a day. Bobwhite quail live for a year in a small group called a covey, which breaks up each spring at courtship time. Once a new covey is formed, the birds travel together and feed within several yards of each other during the day; but at night they roost in close circles with their heads facing outward. This possibly may benefit them in the detection of predators approaching from any direction—certainly it benefits them in the matter of keeping warm in winter.

The advantages of some degree of crowding are numerous. The many eyes of a band of monkeys act as continual sentinels; a flock of birds confuses a pred-

A CIRCLE OF QUAIL

Like pioneers of old in Western movies, a covey of bobwhite quail (above) settles in a protective circle at night. Heads out and tails together, they huddle in low grass or weeds. This circular roosting habit is an organizational adaptation, designed for warmth in autumn and winter as well as for protection from predators. If startled, the quail explode into the air like a feathered bombshell.

atory hawk, which usually can pick off only the laggard or stray bird. Crowding facilitates reproduction by bringing together members of the opposite sex; muskrats, for example, do not breed successfully if their population density falls below the threshold of about one pair per mile of stream or per 86 acres of marshland. Learning by fishes has been shown to be more rapid when the fish are in groups than when individuals are isolated. Aggregations of animals also are capable of modifying the physical conditions under which they live: honeybees air-condition their hives by a mass beating of wings; flatworms in a tight cluster are better protected from the harmful effects of the sun's ultraviolet light than they would be alone—in a group they expose less surface area per worm to the environment. Similarly, groups of goldfish in an experiment survived much longer than isolated individuals in water poisoned by silver nitrate, because the high population proved capable of quickly precipitating the poison and thus detoxifying the water. Gregarious fishes, such as minnows, obtain protection by traveling in schools: if the hindmost minnow is seized by a predatory fish, its skin discharges a substance which is carried through the water and warns the rest of the school of danger.

ANY increase in the abundance of a population must necessarily have consequences not only for the species itself, but also for other populations belonging to the community. There is inevitable danger of local extinction of any population when all its members are concentrated and exposed to the same dangers at the same time. Bacteria put into a dish containing their essential nutrients will multiply rapidly until they deplete the food supply and produce an accumulation of waste products which prevents their further multiplication; in some cases, aquatic animals multiply to such an extent that they exhaust the oxygen supply. Several hundred oyster larvae may all settle on an old shell on the sea bottom, but only a few will find sufficient space to develop into mature oysters. The rest will be killed by overcrowding, although they all apparently try to adjust to crowded conditions by growing in a long, slender form. Elongated oysters are unsuitable for market and that is why oystermen cultivate the beds by breaking apart clusters of young oysters to give them room to develop the rounded form characteristic of uncrowded beds. A recent phenomenon of overcrowding has been noticed at the Philadelphia Zoo, where increased populations of certain mammals during the past eight years may very well have been the cause of a tenfold increase in heart disease among these mammals. No deaths from heart attacks were observed in the mammals until the zoo officials began a program to breed and maintain high populations of some of their captive species. As these populations increased, the relationships among the members became increasingly complex and may have created the stresses that resulted in the high incidence of heart ailments.

The dangers of overcrowding have long been known, but there is also an opposite danger—undercrowding. At all levels of the animal kingdom there is added safety in numbers up to an optimum population level—but there are also adverse effects at a low level. The classic example is the heath hen, a bird that was abundant in the northeastern areas of primeval North America. By 1880, it had been so hounded by man that its entire population was restricted to the single island of Martha's Vineyard, off Cape Cod. A large reservation was established there for the protection of the surviving birds and they actually did increase to about 2,000 birds by 1916. But then a combination of catastrophes occurred—fire, a gale, a severe winter and an unusually heavy visitation by predatory goshawks—which reduced the heath hens to the point where less than 50 breeding pairs survived. This number was obviously below the critical minimum for the species: despite all attempts to build up the tiny flock, the remnant population went into a further decline and the once abundant heath hen finally became extinct in 1932.

Just as important as the mechanisms for survival in determining the ultimate size of a population is the nature of the death rate, for this determines how many individuals will live long enough to reproduce themselves. Although every member of a population must die sooner or later, it is clear that for the success of the population as a whole, later is better than sooner. Each population, of course, may possess a few real oldtimers who have had the good fortune to escape predators and parasites, starvation and inclement weather, competition and accidents—but usually most individuals in a wild population perish long before the time allotted to them by the physiology of their species. However, with an occasional period of unusually favorable conditions, the mortality rate may decline drastically. This quickly leads to overcrowded conditions in the area, a resulting outbreak of disease, starvation—and a subsequent drop in numbers once again.

A great variety of factors contribute to the mortality, or death rate, that serves to put an upper limit on the size of a population. Mortality due to predators, for example, is not simply a matter of an owl grasping a meadow vole in its talons. When meadow voles become abundant, an owl may feed largely on that species. But when the population becomes reduced, the owl will then switch over to alternate prey; these animals then act as buffers until the voles build up their population once again. In short, when voles in general are scarce, individual voles live longer. An alternative to the shortness of life induced by overcrowding is a decrease in the size of the population by emigration of individuals. Studies of the house mouse have shown that when the population flourishes and conditions become congested, some of the mice emigrate to other parts of the house or to nearby structures; those that remain continue their normal rate of reproduction. However, if the overcrowded mice are prevented from emigrating, reproduction is drastically reduced or it may even cease altogether. This is a survival mechanism. Food is used first of all for self-maintenance; reproduction will take place only when the amount of energy intake exceeds that necessary for existence, and when there are other favorable stimuli, such as adequate room for expansion.

IN the same way that life insurance companies compile actuarial tables of the life expectancy of human clients, recent ecological research has attempted to compile life tables for certain kinds of animals. One of these studies was carried on over several years at Mount McKinley National Park, Alaska, with the Dall mountain sheep. Data based on the study of the skulls and horns of 645 dead sheep enabled ecologists to calculate the ages at which the sheep died and to work out an approximate actuarial table for this species—under the special conditions of living in a game preserve and not subject to the depredations of man. The Mount McKinley figures indicate that if one starts with a population of 1,000 mountain sheep, natural mortality will have eliminated 199 of them by the end of the first year. But the life expectancy for the 801 sheep that survive the first year is very good—until they reach about seven years of age, which is the average age of survival of these animals in this environment. Beyond seven years, the death rate rises sharply. The maximum life expectancy in

THE SPAN OF LIFE

Although man has increased the life expectancy of his kind by controlling many natural hazards, he has not been able to prevent aging. Among all warm-blooded animals a potentially longer life is linked to large size, low reproductive rate and slow maturing. Many cold-blooded ones, by contrast, may have no fixed adult size and grow until they die—as most wild animals do—of predation or disease. Theoretically, such an animal, if completely protected, should never die at all.

Below are shown the maximum recorded ages for some representative species.

INVERTEBRATES	YEARS
Silverfish	7
Earthworm	10
Ant Queen	19
Lobster	50
Fresh Water Mussel	100+

FISHES	
Guppy	5
Carp	50+
Halibut	70
Sturgeon	100+

AMPHIBIANS AND REPTILES	
Small Frog	20
Toad	36
Giant Salamander	50+
Alligator	60
Large Tortoise	150+

BIRDS	
Swallow	9
Starling	19
Arctic Tern	27
Domestic Pigeon	35
Ostrich	40
Golden Eagle	80
Vulture	117

MAMMALS	
Shrew	2
Mouse	3
White Rat	4+
Guinea Pig	7+
Rabbit	12
Sheep	15+
Dog	24+
Domestic Cow	30+
Lion	35
Zebra	38+
Hippopotamus	49
Indian Elephant	77+
Man	115+

this environment seems to be about 15 years, and only a few individuals can live that long in the wild state. Under the controlled conditions of zoos, where the sheep are protected from predators and disease, starvation and all the hazards of climate, their physiological life expectancy would no doubt be considerably higher.

The social organization evolved by prairie dogs not only has some obvious value in protecting them against predators, but it also regulates their population density, which minimizes the risk of famine. Some prairie-dog towns are divided by the natural terrain into a number of wards, but the most important subdivisions are the territories of the various clans, or coteries, as they are called. The coterie, which usually occupies approximately seven tenths of an acre, is the basic unit of the town; the members share an elaborate common burrow and the food resources in their territory.

Part of the education of the pups is a knowledge of the extent of the territory. This ensures that it will pass intact from generation to generation even though individual members of a coterie die off or emigrate. Although the neighboring coteries are aggressive toward each other, they cooperate in a common watch for danger in the form of eagles and hawks that swoop from above and from bobcats, coyotes, badgers and ferrets that stalk them on or under the ground. When a prairie dog in any part of the town spots a suspicious movement, it gives a sharp yip, like a small dog. This signal resounds through the town, and all of the animals sit up alert. If the warning call is high-pitched and rapid, they know they have no time to seek the cause of the alarm—they quickly dive into their burrows.

Unlike most rodents, prairie dogs have only one small litter a year; nevertheless the population inevitably increases, and something must be done about this to prevent the disaster of overcrowding and to maintain a fairly level population from year to year. The coterie system takes care of this very neatly. As the population increases, the older generation in the coterie emigrates to the suburbs beyond the borders of the town and establishes a new coterie, leaving the burrow to the younger animals. In cases where an adjacent coterie does not have similar breeding success, emigration to the suburbs is not necessary: the overpopulated coterie merely annexes some of the territory next door. But whichever mechanism operates, the final result is the same—a nearly uniform distribution of the population.

IT is usually the disaster of a large-scale mortality that attracts the attention of man, rather than the year-in, year-out fluctuations of population. These mortalities most often have been connected with the sea, and for as long as man remembers, the coasts of the world have from time to time been suddenly littered with the reeking corpses of fishes, turtles, oysters, shrimps and crabs. There are various causes for mass mortality in the sea: volcanoes, seaquakes and their resulting flood waves, sudden changes in salinity or temperature. But one of the most dramatic and destructive of life in and around the sea is the sudden increase of populations of certain plankton organisms. So populous do these minute organisms become in only a few days that they discolor the water, usually with a red, pink or brown tinge, and thus the plague has long been known as the "red tide." Actually, "red tide" is a misnomer; the mortality, of course, is not caused by the tides, nor is the color of the water always reddish. One of the plagues visited upon Egypt might possibly have been a red tide, for *Exodus* relates: ". . . all the waters that were in the river were turned to blood. And the fish that was in the river died; and the river stank, and the Egyptians could not drink of the water of the river."

Although North America has suffered from red tides along both the Atlantic and Pacific shores, it is along the coast of the Gulf of Mexico that they have been most closely studied. The west coast of Florida has been afflicted at various intervals with no apparent regularity; a red tide was first recorded there in 1844, and in this century alone it has appeared at least nine times, most recently in 1963. Countless millions of dead fish have been deposited on long stretches of beach, bringing commercial and sport fishing to a standstill and posing a threat to the tourist trade. It was not until 1947 that scientists identified the specific organism that was causing the mass mortality off Florida. It is a microscopic dinoflagellate which stands on the razor's edge that separates plant from animal among the lower organisms. This minute creature is usually very scarce, but it can multiply rapidly to the point where 6,000 of them may be found in a single drop of water.

IN the Florida studies, it was learned that a combination of events is necessary to bring about this sudden increase, called a "bloom." It includes heavy rains which wash specific trace elements from the land into the coastal waters, a lowered salinity of the water, a particular water temperature and an absence of wind. When all of these conditions occur at a single time along the coast, the dinoflagellates are triggered to divide rapidly: a single cell can potentially produce 33 million individuals after only 25 divisions. These dinoflagellates release into the water a deadly toxin that partially paralyzes the nervous systems of fishes and other forms of marine life and ultimately kills them. Even small droplets of the poisoned water—tossed up in the form of spray by breakers along the beach—can cause severe respiratory irritations in humans. The interactions causing the bloom are extraordinarily subtle. Laboratory experiments have revealed that whether or not a bloom occurs may depend on differences as small as one part per million in the concentrations of iron, zinc, cobalt or other elements in the water. The problem of predicting or controlling these damaging red tides is further complicated by the fact that some types of dinoflagellates, when they find conditions favorable for blooming, secrete substances that inhibit the growth of related species that might also flourish under the same conditions.

The rise and fall of the various red tide dinoflagellates demonstrates the complexity of the ecology of the ocean. Even when their populations are low, dinoflagellates remain an invisible menace. Certain shellfish seem to possess the capacity to store up the dinoflagellate poison. This concentrated poison can make shellfish dangerous to humans that eat them, as was demonstrated by the outbreak of mass poisoning which affected 40,000 people during a recent five-year period in the Pacific regions. But ecologists who have studied the problem believe it is more complex than the mere harboring of poison by the shellfish—it may involve an intricate meshing of several species: coral polyps, their symbiotic algae and various fishes. Certain corals, to cite one example, appear to enter into partnership with algae, at least some of which may be dinoflagellates in disguise—of a poisonous variety. In the intricate food chains of the reef, the dinoflagellates are passed along to small fishes which eat the coral and, in turn, become poisonous to other fishes that prey upon them. However, this is somewhat speculative, as it is also possible that the poisonous dinoflagellates do not enter into partnerships, but rather are free-living around the

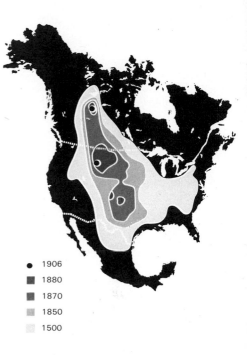

● 1906
■ 1880
■ 1870
1850
1500

WHERE BUFFALO ROAMED

When Columbus discovered America, the boundaries of buffalo country (shown on map above) stretched from New York to Oregon and into Canada and Mexico. By the beginning of the 19th Century, the animals had almost disappeared east of the Mississippi. As settlers and railroads moved westward, the remaining range was cut drastically. By 1906, the wild buffalo grounds had dwindled to two tiny areas in Yellowstone Park and near Canada's Lake Athabasca.

reefs. Upwellings of water containing the necessary elements could trigger their blooms, starting the sequence by which the toxins pass on to the coral animals and shellfish which feed on the dinoflagellates, and then up the food chain, ultimately to man.

Mass mortality is nothing new on this planet, which has seen not only mortalities of populations, but also mass extinctions of worldwide species. Of the 2,500 families of animals that have been discovered in the fossil record, roughly two thirds have died out without leaving descendants. One does not have to go back to the dinosaurs or the trilobites to find examples of mass extinction. Between about 6,000 and 10,000 years ago, the following impressive list of large mammals became extinct in North America alone: the mastodon, Columbian mammoth, dire wolf, camel, horse, giant armadillo, two kinds of bison, giant ground sloth, a tapir and the woolly mammoth. In fact, in the past 12,000 years, roughly three quarters of the North American large herbivores have disappeared.

Numerous theories have been offered to account for these mass extinctions and they include climate change, predation by Indians, catastrophic changes in the earth, racial old age. Most of these theories are impossible to prove and will always remain theories, but the ecologist can offer a possible answer in the intimate relationships among living things. All the organisms in a complex food chain are vulnerable to any physical change that strikes at the base of the pyramid, the primary producer. Climatic change alone could not have caused directly the mass extinction of the herbivores of North America; but climatic change that affected the producers, the grasses themselves, could have sent up through all the successive levels of the food pyramid quakes severe enough to eventually topple it.

After the great dying of North American herbivores, an intricately interwoven grazing community had arisen again by the time of the arrival of European man. It supported some 60 million bison, as well as great herds of pronghorn antelopes, both of which were preyed upon by wolves and coyotes. There was an abundant population of small mammals that burrowed in the ground; there were specialized insects, and birds modified for strong flight against the winds of open country as well as for running on the ground. Niches were filled and subdivided into smaller niches, eventually producing ecological systems of great complexity.

THIS superstructure of life has largely been overthrown by man, not only by bison hunts, by poisoned bait and trap, but primarily by striking at the very base of the ecological pyramid—by rearranging habitats. To the grassland community and the now virtually extinct wolf, bison and prairie dog, man's arrival was a catastrophe perhaps equivalent to the geological catastrophes of the past, only it was more swift. The vulnerable grassland has now been replaced by neat checkerboard squares of wheat and corn, and the indigenous animals today exist largely in the living museums of the national parks and monuments. Among the major catastrophes suffered by animals in the billions of years of life on earth—the dying out of trilobites some 250 million years ago, of dinosaurs some 60 million years ago, the mass extinctions about two to three million years ago at the close of the Pliocene, the disappearance of many large mammals of North America and Eurasia about 10,000 years ago—among all these, surely future millennia will list as a major natural disaster the establishment in North America of European man.

BULL BISON, BATTLING AT THE RUTTING SEASON, SHOW THE RENEWED VITALITY OF THE HERDS WHICH SO RECENTLY WERE ALMOST EXTINCT

Tragedy on the Plains

Basic to the Great Plains of North America were the grasses on which all creatures there, from the Indians down to the smallest insects, ultimately depended. Civilized man destroyed these primary producers with an efficiency matched only by his shortsightedness. The vital life cycle of the Plains was changed forever—a tragedy dramatically exemplified in the fate of the bison herds.

BISON   DIAMONDBACK RATTLESNAKE   PRAIRIE DOG   BURROWING OWLS

The Prairie: Life in Balance

Before the white man arrived on the Great Plains of North America, nature through millennia had evolved a balance. The land easily supported a wonderful variety of living creatures, many competing with each other to survive, yet all to some extent dependent on one another. Scattered widely across the

PRAIRIE DOGS   WOLVES   PRONGHORN

prairies, shown here rolling toward the misty foothills of
the Rockies, herds of bison and pronghorn grazed on the lush
grama and buffalo grass. They seldom lingered in one place
long enough to damage the area by overgrazing. Packs of
wolves kept the herds on the move and pruned them down by
preying on the young and the infirm. Pockmarking the landscape were towns of prairie dogs which fed on the nutritious
grasses and the seeds of many herbs. Feeding on the prairie
dogs were a host of predators, including the rattlesnake and
the burrowing owl, which often took over burrows of its victims.

WESTERN JACK RABBIT   COYOTES   COLUMBIAN GROUND SQUIRREL   WESTERN RAVEN   LONGHORN CATTLE

The Prairie: Life Unbalanced

Jack rabbits, ground squirrels and many other smaller animals flourished on the Great Plains, but each species' natural tendency to multiply was constantly checked by available food and by predators. The Indians themselves, largely nomadic, adjusted to the natural order. But the white settlers saw wealth

13-STRIPED GROUND SQUIRREL   WHITE-FACED HEREFORDS   COLUMBIAN GROUND SQUIRREL

in the grasslands in the form of cattle and sheep. They killed off the competing herds of pronghorn and bison. Predators were poisoned, as were the prairie dogs into whose holes the cattle stumbled, often breaking their legs. Birds feeding off poisoned carcasses, like the raven eating the dead coyote above, were poisoned in turn. Insects and small rodents on which the birds had fed then multiplied and the land suffered devastating plagues. Cattle overgrazed the range, and sheep nibbled the grasses to their roots. The biome was torn apart, erosion set in and large areas of the once-rich plains turned into deserts.

MAKING THE KILL, a hunter aims his lance at a running bull. Although horses, an unintended gift from the conquistadors, completely changed the Indians' way of life by enabling them to meet the swift buffalo on their own terms, the numbers that they killed before traders gave them guns were still far less than the toll taken by natural enemies and the harsh climate.

The Bison—an Epic Dying

Bison are wary beasts; their sense of smell is excellent, their hearing acute. A herd posts sentinels, and when danger threatens it runs. In the beginning, Indian nomads of the Plains had hunted them on foot with stone, lance and arrow, occasionally stampeding whole herds over cliffs but more often content with a carcass or two, stalked with infinite care. The Plains Indians might, if the hunt had gone well, barter a few skins with the wealthy agricultural tribes to the south, such as the Pueblos. When the conquistadors came to Mexico, they brought with them fleet horses, and by the late 17th Century the Plains Indians, having broken the wild, wandering descendants of these Spanish mounts, were using them to chase the buffalo across the Plains. The braves took fierce pride in their new skill. A 19th Century observer describes a spring hunt thus: "The high chief has a lance, with a handle six feet and a blade three feet in length. This in hand, he rides boldly to the side of the flying buffalo and thrusts it again and again through the liver or heart of one and then another of the affrighted herd." Thus the poor nomad became the dashing master of the territory. From the buffalo he took his food and lodging, his clothing, bedding and fuel, strings for his bow, glue for his arrows, thread, cordage, harnesses for his horses, saddle pads, vessels to hold water, boats to cross streams. Though wasteful in his hunting habits, he still made no serious inroad on the bovine hordes—until the great fur companies came on the scene, with tempting offers of barter for buffalo hides. This was the beginning of the end: from now on, white man and Indian were to join in one of the greatest animal slaughters of all time.

To the Brink of Extinction

The first Europeans to penetrate North America, the Spaniards, found herds of bison in Mexico and called them "wild cows." The French met them in Canada and used their own word, *boeuf*. Englishmen likened them to Africa's water buffalo and gave them their most common name. Wherever the place, whatever the name, the reaction was the same: the bison were shot—reasonably at first, for food and clothing, later in a kind of madness.

What motivated the slaughter? No doubt part of the answer lay in the sheer numbers of the animals. The bison population had been steadily expanding since the last ice age. Wandering animals, their

THE BISON was first seen by white men in 1521, when Cortez visited Montezuma's menagerie in Mexico. This picture, dated 1553, is one of the earliest such published.

BY MID-1870, as this engraving from *Harper's Weekly* shows, buffalo were systematically hounded, like this herd being driven into the Missouri. The average annual kill had reached 250,000—but sometimes that many were killed in a month.

SPECIAL TRAINS, like this one on the Kansas Pacific line, were run for buffalo hunters, complete with refreshments for the weary. Many railroads ran through buffalo country, and passengers found easy sport by shooting animals from windows.

RAW HIDES were pegged out to dry before being baled and shipped East. Early hunters took only winter robes, allowing the herds a respite during rutting season, but a growing demand for hides as leather soon made bison a year-round mark.

AFTER THE ORGY, bleached skeletons covered the Plains. Ironically, even these found their uses: wagoners hauling freight from railheads would pick them up on their way in. Bones were made into fertilizer, horns into buttons and combs.

THE GREATEST KILLER, the Sharp's .45-caliber, center-fire rifle, was introduced to the game in the early '80s. With it a skilled hunter could kill a buffalo at 400 yards.

search for pasture had brought them east as far as New York, west to the Rockies, north into Canada as far as the Great Slave Lake and south into Mexico as far as Monterrey—60 million head is the conservative count at the time when the Thirteen Colonies were struggling for a foothold on the edge of the continent. By the time Grover Cleveland was moving into the White House for a second term in 1893, there were about 1,090 left. Most of the millions were killed in about 70 years—from 1820 to 1889. Food, profit, policy (to undermine the Indians) and fun all played their part. Wrote E. Douglas Branch, the 20th Century historian, one of the first to chronicle the mass killing: "It was an awful, epic hunt."

MILITARY COMMANDER of the Southwest in the '70s, General Phil Sheridan felt that killing buffalo was the best way to solve the Indian problem.

THE LAST STAND of General George A. Custer was made in 1876 against Sioux warriors made desperate by the buffalo killing and advance of the railroads.

BILLY TILGHMAN shot a record 3,300 buffalo in seven months. Hunters tried for a "stand," killing the leader and sentinels first, then the rest one by one.

BUFFALO BILL CODY, his magnificently trained horse Brigham, his rifle "Lucretia Borgia," and a few half-tamed bison glorified the old days for later generations. Cody, no fake, was an ex-army scout who killed 4,280 buffalo for railroad gangs.

THE NUCLEUS of a herd, 15 bison in crates (six males and nine females) were sent in 1907 by the New York Zoological Society to the Wichita Forest and Game Preserve. By then the bison had been virtually extinct for 20 years. The herd thrived.

159

The Revitalized Herds

Bills to protect the buffalo were presented to Congress as early as 1871, but, opposed by such authorities as Secretary of the Interior Columbus Delano, who believed that the Indian could best be subdued by killing off the herds, the bills were either never passed or at best ended up in a presidential pigeonhole. In 1886, William T. Hornaday, chief taxidermist of the National Museum at Washington, D.C., found traces of about 600 wild buffalo, including a much smaller herd which had taken refuge in Yellowstone Park. His report shocked many in Washington who, now that the Indian was no longer a threat, could afford to be shocked. But still nothing was done. By the spring of 1894, after a hard winter and severe poaching by hunters, who at worst faced the penalty of eviction from the park if they were caught, a count showed that the Yellowstone herd had dwindled to 20 head. Thereupon, a bill was finally passed imposing a stiff fine and imprisonment on anyone convicted of killing a buffalo within park limits. This was the very first action taken by Washington to protect the American bison. Later, stocked

A BUFFALO HERD ROAMS THE ARIZONA PLAINS OF TODAY. WATCHED OVER BY A RANGER, WITHOUT NATURAL PREDATORS, PROTECTED AS WELL AS

from eastern zoos and the show herds of wealthy cattlemen, additional herds were established on preserves. Today there are more than 9,000 bison in the U.S.; a very large herd, which missed the worst of the slaughter and was protected earlier by law, exists in Canada. All the herds are growing again and must be kept rigidly under control so as not to exceed the carrying capacity of their range. Buffalo cows mature at two or three years, and although they bear only one calf each spring, they remain fertile through a life span which may reach 40 years.

A LONE TROPHY is hoisted onto a truck as an Arizona hunting party watches. State law now allows a man only one buffalo in his lifetime; applications to shoot are backlogged for years.

CONFINED BY FENCES, THE HERD WOULD SOON OUTGROW ITS RANGE IF NOT CUT BACK EACH YEAR BY CONTROLLED SHOOTING OF A SELECT NUMBER

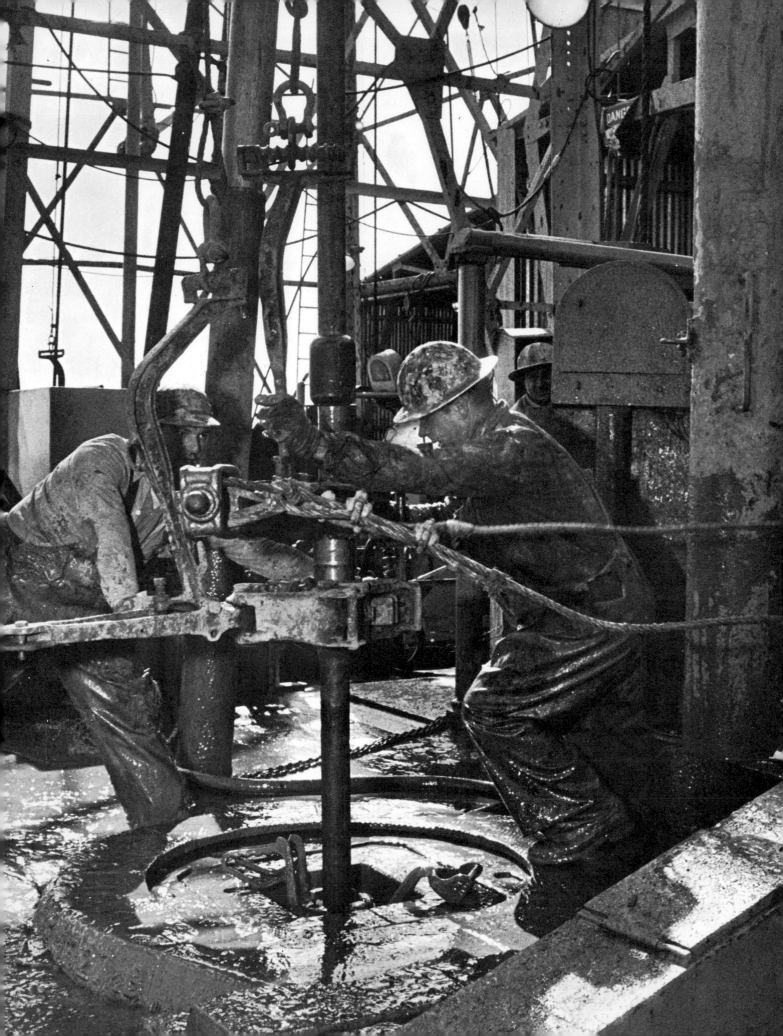

8

Man versus Nature

THE despair felt by many people as they look upon a world drastically altered by the hand of man was rarely more deeply expressed than in the lines by Thomas Beddoes, an English poet of the last century:

> *Nature's polluted,*
> *There's man in every secret corner of her*
> *Doing damned wicked deeds. Thou art, old world*
> *A hoary, atheistic, murdering star.*

And truly, modern man, with his atomic gadgetry and penchant for uprooting the earth, does seem to have severed his intimate ties with the natural world. It is this unnatural break that makes many a modern man hanker for a primitive and simpler past, or for the remote civilizations that still persist in close harmony with nature. It is indeed true that primitive man more fully, although unknowingly, used ecological principles in his everyday life. He usually did not make the distinction modern man does—between himself and the surrounding natural world, as if all else in nature outside of man's body could be lumped together. Although the word "totem" comes from the language of the Ojibway Indians, who lived around the Great Lakes, the idea of totemism is found in primitive cultures around the world. Totemism generally means a sense of kinship between a group of people and a particular object or form of life, whether it be the parrot fish totem of an aboriginal clan in Australia or the tiger of a clan in India. Perhaps the idea of totemism persists unconsciously in this more complicated modern world, for its modern relic may be the symbols of today's nations, invariably an animal supposed to possess enviable attributes— the United States eagle, the Russian bear, the British lion.

Many supposedly primitive peoples do possess an impressive body of ecological insight. The South American Indians of the equatorial forest know their environment intimately—the places frequented by every kind of animal and the best ways to catch it, the names of the different trees and their attributes; the Masai of East Africa have been aware for centuries that mosquito bites cause malaria; the Eskimo long ago discovered that his sledge dogs were susceptible to the diseases of the wild arctic foxes. The Buddhist tradition in Asia protects animals because Buddha revered all forms of life and would not tolerate cruelty; as a result, the lands surrounding Buddhist monasteries in many cases have become virtual wildlife sanctuaries. An extreme of this tradition is Jainism: the Jain monk, bound to respect even the lives of insects, carries a broom to sweep them aside lest he tread on them accidentally. That this kinship with the world of nature has persisted, despite the attempts of Western man to extirpate it, was demonstrated when attempts were made to control rats in warehouses in India; the natives placed in charge persisted in leaving water for the rats to drink. It is easy for Western men to ridicule these beliefs as sentimental or even foolish. Yet the great modern theologian and humanist, Dr. Albert Schweitzer, echoes this essential reverence for all living things: "The great fault of all ethics hitherto has been that they believed themselves to have to deal only with the relation of man to man."

W HERE then did man go astray in cleaving the ties of his heritage with the rest of nature? Although no one knows for sure, the process probably began in Asia Minor a scant 10,000 years ago—a mere 375 human generations— during the Neolithic, also called the New Stone Age because improved stone tools were then used by man. The preneolithic peoples, although few in number, interfered with their environment on a scale out of proportion to their scarcity. Some of their hunting methods were sheer waste, such as driving herds of animals over precipices as an easy way of killing them. Since his population was low and he was constantly on the move, however, man's influence on the environment was local and only temporary—giving the land time to recover until man came that way again. The onset of the Neolithic was probably not a sudden economic revolution; rather agriculture and domestication of animals must have emerged gradually out of the Mesolithic. But these tendencies gathered momentum in the Neolithic; it was then that man clearly emerged as the only animal that set out to subdue his environment instead of adapting to it.

Neolithic man interfered with nature by growing crops and turning animals to his use—thus inevitably destroying forests, causing soil to wash away, polluting rivers with sediment, accelerating the natural and gradual processes of erosion and plant succession. To prepare the fields and harvest the crops, to care for the animals, to process the foodstuffs and animal byproducts, required a communal life of closely packed villages rather than small nomadic tribes. As the intricacy of the village system grew, it was soon found that one village might have a good supply of stone for axes, another of clay for pottery, a third of plant

MAN AND MANTIS

For the Asmat tribe of New Guinea, the praying mantis (at left on the carved wood canoe prow above) is the totemic emblem of man. Why? Not only because it resembles the figure of a man, but also because the Asmats, until recently, were cannibals, preying on men as the mantis does on insects. Similarly symbolic are the bills of the berry-eating hornbill bird (on the right). To these ex-head-hunters, the berries represent their victims' heads.

fibers for baskets. These products were distributed by trade, which necessitated making roads. It was only a logical extension of these tendencies that has resulted in today's complex of metropolises, the destruction of primeval forests, our stress-causing social patterns—and a modern view of nature as something to be subjugated, not as an abundance with which to live in harmony.

The neolithic way of life persists today, most conspicuously in the headwaters of the impenetrable Amazonian forests, in the interior of New Guinea, among the Berber tribesmen of North Africa. Somewhat less conspicuously, the Neolithic still exists even in the so-called developed countries, where farm lands cluster around a village. Man still cuts forests haphazardly and plows deep into natural grasslands, and in many even rather advanced places his faith in wonder cures and religious healing differs little from a primitive faith in the shaman who used herbs and magic to cure human diseases. "Neolithic culture is much more than a subject of inquiry by prehistorians," states the anthropologist Carlton S. Coon. "Moving out of it may be the world's most difficult problem."

Ever since the Neolithic, man has had the power—and the responsibility—of a destiny ascribed to him in *Genesis:* to "have dominion over all the earth." But during his dominion he has broken nearly every ecological principle of energy flow, isolation, community interaction and population control—and so far he seems to have gotten away with it. He has misused land, forests, water, sea fisheries; he has spread diseases and alien forms of life, at the same time extirpating native forms; in recent centuries he has been reproducing like the lemming and introducing too many of his own kind into ecosystems that cannot hold them. The fact that man's present state in the world is adjudged perilous can be seen by the hair-raising titles of some books published in the last few decades—written not by cranks but by scientists and humanists deeply concerned about the human conditions—*Road to Survival*, *The Rape of the Earth*, *Our Plundered Planet*, *The Geography of Hunger*, *The Limits of the Earth*, *The Prevalence of People*, and many others.

In fact, by the 20th Century, man had finally conquered the biosphere and colonized the earth. His domination is due to his brain, and appropriately it has been suggested by one scientist that the new state of the biosphere be referred to as the noösphere—derived from the Greek word for "mind."

Modern man must soon make a decision. Either he will abide by technology and live in a man-centered planet in which he becomes increasingly aloof from several billion years of biological experiences—or he will work in harmony with the principles of ecology and use for himself the same criteria that apply to plants and other animals. The choice is not a simple one. The engineer assures us that he can control nature, the ecologist states that he can live in harmony with it—and both views can be sustained by argument. But the viewpoint of this book has been that man belongs *to* nature and cannot long remain separate from various biological laws without an eventual day of reckoning—that he must develop what the American conservationist Aldo Leopold called an "ecological conscience." Following the ecological viewpoint, let us see some of the primary principles that man is challenging, and their possible consequences.

In the first place, man has markedly altered the physical environment itself—as do all living things. But whereas the changes in environment promoted by other living things encourage renewal and turnover, man has in many cases disrupted the opportunities for rebirth. While man remained simply a food gatherer, he caused little modification of the environment, and the turnover was rapid. At this stage, he might be considered as a commensal with his environment as a whole. The Indians of the Great Plains of North America, for example, fitted in quite well with the grassland community. They were high-level consumers of the bison and did not much upset the intricate relationship between producing grasses and the primary consumers, the bison, or the wolves that preyed upon them. However, as soon as man reached the level of domestication and agriculture, he began to change the environment physically. He struggled against the regrowth of natural vegetation and thus prevented the successional stages of vegetation to the climax. In planting crops and breeding animals, he made certain species dependent upon him for their survival—wheat cannot now procreate by itself, and a cow abandoned on the plains would in a short time fall prey to coyotes. Man has converted the cow from a wild animal, well able to defend itself and its young, into a walking milk factory.

As man progressed to the next level, that of industry, he went even further—he created a whole new ecosystem and substituted it for the natural one. A dam thrown across a river alters the entire natural drainage pattern and thereby upsets the water tables of the area. The toxic fumes from smelters have utterly destroyed all life for miles around them, creating such man-made deserts as those once caused in southeastern Tennessee by copper mining and at Sudbury, Ontario, by nickel fumes. In the latest state—urbanization—man has completely replaced all of the natural elements in the environment with artificial ones. Instead of soil, natural water systems, plant and animal communities, there now exist concrete surfaces, sewage pipes, and parks composed largely of alien plants and animals. In urban centers man has virtually suppressed all life that ever existed there and has substituted a community of little variety that repeats itself in cities around the world. Usually the only animals that live with man in this urban environment are his domesticated dogs, cats, goldfish, turtles, canaries, budgies and a few other pets. The birds found in the North American urban environment are either aliens—street pigeons, starlings, English sparrows —or the few natives that have been able to adapt to urban living in parks of foreign vegetation. In the cities there also live man's unwelcome congeners: rats, houseflies, cockroaches, lice and numerous microorganisms. During the various steps up to urbanization, man has so radically altered the face of the earth—the very physical environment to which life had gradually become adapted—that any repopulation by the original plants and animals is remote indeed.

Hand in hand with the alteration of the physical environment went the disruption of the original community. A natural community in an area that has not seen sudden geologic change is a tight fabric of food webs which are connected with the environment. Man has simplified and rearranged the energy relationship that once prevailed in these communities; he has eliminated complicating threads from the fabric of life to such an extent that in many places it is threadbare indeed. Primitive man was a second- or third-order consumer—he lived off other animals that had first consumed the plant producer, or off the predatory animals that consumed the herbivores. When he gathered fruits and nuts he was a first-order consumer, but with the advent of agriculture he broadened his food sources, substituting edible plants for inedible pine needles and oak leaves. He simplified natural grasslands by growing wheat, corn, potatoes, cassava and other crops in a single-crop system. To meet his demands for wood, he replaced the luxuriant deciduous forests with quick-growing conifers. He satisfied his taste for meat by growing food for his domesticated herbivores, such as sheep and cattle. To make himself secure as a first-order consumer, he not only had to shorten the natural food chains but also eliminate whatever predators he believed to be in conflict with his interests.

Because insects consume his food crops and his ornamental flowers as well, man has broadcast upon the landscape insecticides that eliminate not only his direct competitors, but many beneficial and abounding noncompetitive forms of life as well. Without quite realizing it, he has thus left himself vulnerable. For this kind of simplified biological community—such as exists naturally on certain remote islands or in the tundra—can be upset much more easily when one of its parts gets out of kilter than can a diversified community. Wheat stretching as far as the eye can see undoubtedly can be harvested more efficiently by machines; but a single crop of wheat is also susceptible to sudden onslaughts of insects or fungi which can build up their populations catastrophically in a short time. Man is constantly on guard against creatures he thought he had subdued, for uneasy lies the crown of husbandry where even a small population of potential usurpers still exists. The only way man has been able to produce successful wheat crops is by always staying one small step ahead of the blight of rust—by turning out new varieties of wheat faster than the fungus can adapt to them. And he has found that one peculiar fact about the use of insecticides is that they actually encourage other pests. In recent years DDT has been applied widely in orchards around the world for the control of certain pests, among them red mites that attack fruit. But instead of killing red mites, DDT kills its enemies without much harming the mite itself. As a result, there has arisen the new problem of a worldwide abundance of red mites in orchards.

There is no denying that in general the man-made community works efficiently—though it may continue to do so for only a limited time. Nevertheless, this efficiency has allowed man to circumvent another set of ecological principles, those governing populations. Today there are some three billion human beings on the planet. About 270,000 infants are born every day, and about 142,000 people die every day—making a surplus of some 128,000 daily, or a population increase each month equivalent to that of Chicago. When Christ was born there were probably between 250 and 350 million people on earth. It was not until 1650 that this number doubled; in only 200 years after that it doubled again; and in the mere hundred years between 1850 and 1950 it doubled once more. Unless one believes that man has utterly obliterated the biosphere and substituted for it a successful noösphere, then this sort of population increase cannot continue much longer. If the annual rate of human growth were to continue at its present 1.8 per cent, by 1980 there would be close to another billion people —and not long after the year 2000 the world population would double today's.

Only during the relatively last few seconds of man's short tenure on earth has the human population increase become a problem. The maximum worldwide human population during paleolithic times probably did not exceed 10 million; this number started to rise with the coming of the neolithic revolution, when agriculture made it possible for the land to support a higher population. One of the first people to become concerned was Thomas Malthus, who published his *Essay on Population* in 1798; at that time the human population was less than a third of what it is today. Malthus' approach was a sound ecological one. He calculated that human populations possess the biotic potential to double every 25 years but that food resources do not multiply so rapidly. Therefore, human population, unless held in check, will increase up to the very limit of its food

THE DEADLY AUTO ENGINE

Of all the various agents of air pollution, the gasoline engines powering the world's millions of automobiles are among the most difficult to control. The toxic, unburned hydrocarbons in crank-

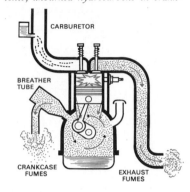

case fumes (above) could be fairly easily (and cheaply: $5 to $10) eliminated by a "blowby" recycler, which feeds them back from the breather tube into the carburetor (below) so that they are burned in the engine cylinders. More complicated

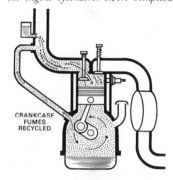

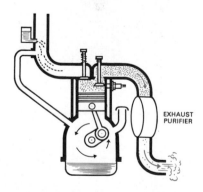

are systems to detoxify the exhaust fumes themselves (above): these may employ either a catalyst for low-temperature (200° to 1,500° F.) combustion, or an "after-burner" which, like a blowtorch, burns the hydrocarbons at temperatures around 2,800° F. The real problem: to win approval of such devices by car owners.

supply. The only logical answer to what he called this "dismal theorem" was human misery. It was fashionable to deride Malthus during the optimism that swept the 19th Century, and there are still optimists today who state that Malthus was wrong. The fact is that Malthus has been proven correct more than once: in Ireland in the early 19th Century, the introduction of the potato, a cheap and easily raised staple food, brought on a population explosion that was finally halted by the potato blight and resulting famine in 1845. In India today, constant famine graphically demonstrates the inability of the environment to keep pace with human growth. Some 10,000 people around the world die every day of starvation or malnutrition. Despite agricultural advances, irrigation and reclamation of deserts, more than half of the world's population still lives in perpetual hunger. Only the Western civilizations have seemingly escaped the workings of the dismal theorem by their present agricultural abundance. However, Malthus has not been disproved by Western technology; there merely has not been time as yet for the truth of his dismal theorem to be tested.

THE entire question of the future size of human populations is enveloped in unknowns. No one is certain how far future technology can increase the carrying capacity of the planet for man, nor can one be sure that future population growth will not exceed even the advances of technology. In populations of other animals, there are controls built into the ecosystem in the form of competition, starvation, predation and disease. But man rightly does everything in his power to prevent these ecological controls from operating upon the human population and causing human suffering. He tries to keep diseases from creating violent population fluctuations such as occurred during the Middle Ages when about a fourth of Europe's population died from the Black Death. He has long ago eliminated predation by other animals as a factor in human population control. He has made almost continuous attempts to eliminate competition within his own species by trying to outlaw war. With the checks upon human populations largely removed, man has increasingly relied upon new technology to provide for his constantly growing numbers. But the technological opportunities—controlling the climate, growing algae for food in artificial ponds, desalting the seas —all have their limits and at best they can only buy time until man works out some way of controlling his own numbers by himself.

One of the startling revelations of the last United States census was that Vermont had not increased its population, a fact that led an eminent Vermonter, the poet Robert Frost, to say that he was glad it had not. "We want to grow right," he stated. Growing right means that man should possess the amenities of life in the form of open space, a diet of meat rather than algae, of water for recreation rather than solely for efficient fish farming. Among these amenities is the one of living on a planet sufficiently uncrowded for other forms of life to exist. The grizzly bear has been hounded nearly to extinction and a mere 1,000 survive in the United States proper, plus 5,000 more in remote areas of Alaska. There is something that strikes at the ecological conscience here; it is not sufficient that the grizzly should survive only as a relict species in the distant north. "Relegating grizzlies to Alaska is about like relegating happiness to heaven," wrote Aldo Leopold, "one may never get there."

At this time man simply does not have the necessary information to make sound judgments about his future; ironically, he knows less about the laws governing the rises and falls of his own populations than he does about those of many other kinds of animals. But fever, famine and war are still the three basic

THE POPULATION EXPLOSION

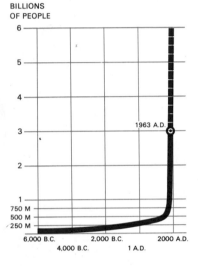

BILLIONS
OF PEOPLE

1963 A.D.

6,000 B.C.   2,000 B.C.   2000 A.D.
   4,000 B.C.   1 A.D.

PEOPLE PER SQUARE MILE

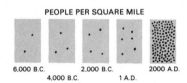

6,000 B.C.   2,000 B.C.   2000 A.D.
   4,000 B.C.   1 A.D.

The graph shown here traces the gradual increase in human numbers over thousands of years, leading up to the vast explosion which is currently under way. In the last century the population has doubled and in another half century it may double again (dotted line), conjuring up the frightening image shown in the squares below of 125 individuals per square mile of the earth, compared to about six per square mile in 1 A.D. Even now the overload is worse than these averages indicate. Only one tenth of the earth is arable, and most of the croplands lie outside of Asia—yet half of the world's people are concentrated there.

controls upon human numbers. Despite man's best efforts, war looms as an everyday possibility, and hunger is a reality to half of the world. Seemingly, the control of infectious diseases marks man's greatest success in eliminating the checks upon his numbers. But man's discovery of the microbial world and his attempts to control it have brought with it ecological disruptions. Although microbes have not yet been used as weapons of war, they have been used in what is known as the "biological control" of species that man regards as pests. In Australia in 1950 and thereafter in western Europe, the virus of myxomatosis from Brazil decreased the rabbit hordes without harm to other species. The unleashing of insect pathogens against insect pests has been gaining momentum in recent years and, if used wisely, can be an ecological alternative to the widespread spraying of insecticides. But there is also danger in spreading these pathogens on the landscape, for this exposes whole populations of animals to the impact of strains of pathogens that did not evolve and reach their present density by natural processes.

Until the 1945 atomic blast at Alamogordo, no animal in a natural environment had been exposed to the effects of radiation beyond the low background level that always has been part of the terrestrial surroundings. In recent years man has released radiation into the environment in tremendous amounts, with effects upon individuals, populations, communities and ecosystems that cannot yet be assessed. Radioactive substances raining down upon the landscape after an atomic test penetrate the soils and water; many organisms absorb them and concentrate them in their tissues. So far, the dilute amounts found in the environment are probably of no serious consequence, but there are grounds for deep concern. Very little is known about the exact effects of low-level, long-term exposure to radiation upon ecosystems, but facts are available about the effect of radioactivity due to X-rays. One fact stands out clearly: there are substantial differences among organisms in their ability to tolerate massive doses. Ten thousand rads—units of absorbed dose—may change the rate at which bacteria in a culture divide, but it might take more than a million rads to kill all the bacteria. The mammals, which are generally more susceptible, can be affected by doses as low as 100 and killed by 1,000 rads. But even these figures are misleading, for living things vary in their sensitivity at different stages of their life cycle. A dose of 163 rads will kill half of the eggs of the fruit fly during cell division—but 100,000 are necessary to kill half of a larger population of fruit fly adults. Radiation thus acts as a strainer upon the ecosystem, tending to destroy certain types more rapidly than others.

THIS selectivity means that if a community is exposed to a higher level of radiation than the insignificant background radiation under which it evolved, large-scale disruptions could take place. Sensitive strains or species would be eliminated, and there would inevitably have to be adaptations and adjustments to fill the niches left vacant. For example, when predator and prey populations of different species of mites were irradiated equally, it was found that the predator population was more sensitive than the prey; the result was that with the control upon their numbers removed, the prey species suddenly increased. There could well be a plague of them unless other predatory species—of necessity also unharmed by the radiation—could step in and fill the niche left by the irradiation of the predatory mites. It is possible that at the present time man is producing by radiation similar ecological explosions of certain species.

Even if small doses of radioisotopes are introduced into the air or water, they

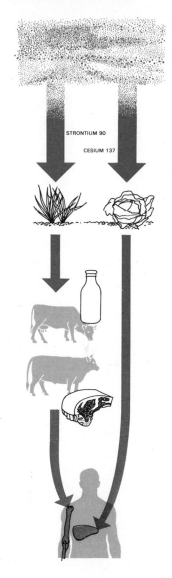

STRONTIUM 90

CESIUM 137

The core of the fallout problem lies not so much in the quantity of fallout but in the way certain long-lived radioactive particles become concentrated in the course of a food chain. Thus the radioisotope strontium 90 is absorbed by cattle as they eat tainted grass; it is passed on to man via milk and meat, and, like calcium, finally concentrates in the bone marrow, where it may lead to leukemia or bone cancer. Cesium 137, less soluble, is picked up directly from vegetables and concentrates in soft tissues such as the liver or gonads, where it may be a menace to the genes, bearers of heredity.

may undergo unexpected concentrations, with far-reaching effects on food chains—an individual high in the food chain may then represent a lethal package to the final consumer. This was demonstrated at the Hanford atomic power plant on the Columbia River in Washington, where minute amounts of various isotopes were released into the water at a constant rate, making it possible to measure the way in which radioactivity might become concentrated in food chains under natural conditions. One of the measurements made by the Hanford scientists revealed that the eggs of ducks and geese contained radioactive phosphorus in concentrations averaging 200,000 times higher than the solution released into the water—and occasionally the concentration soared as high as 1,500,000 times. In another case, of air contamination, iodine became concentrated in the thyroids of jack rabbits at an average level 500 times as great as released. These levels may not yet be critical for the organisms concerned; despite the high concentrations of phosphorus in the waterfowl eggs, the eggs still hatched. There is, however, little knowledge of the genetic damage caused to the species, although it certainly exists. If present pollution of the environment by radioactivity persists, a threshold will soon be reached beyond which serious damage will be done to the ecosystem by the elimination of sensitive organisms. Even barring nuclear holocaust and further testing of atomic bombs, man's peaceful uses of atomic energy alone will create a garbage disposal problem of the nuclear wastes into the environment.

As man looks about him at the noösphere he has created, he is tempted to call a moratorium on technology and give himself the opportunity for needed soul searching, hopefully to come up with the answers to problems that threaten his very survival. But stopping the clock does not solve ecological problems any more than closing the banks solves economic ones. In ecology there are no Gardens of Eden, no Utopias, no ways of turning the clock back to a simpler existence. It is, in fact, probably of the essence of the human animal that he consciously pursues change. This has set him apart from the rest of the natural world by leading him to abandon the tropical environment to which he was biologically adapted, and has brought him ultimately to the changes he has wrought during his bid for control of nature. Charles Darwin in *The Descent of Man* recognized the human need for change and its biological implications: "If all our women were to become as beautiful as the Venus de' Medici, we should for a time be charmed; but we should soon wish for variety; and as soon as we had obtained variety, we should wish to see certain characters a little exaggerated." Man's estate seemingly is to live with unsatisfied aspirations; it is what has led to his present predicament of being a ruler over the earth without knowing the rules.

However, these rules do exist in an ecological view of the world and of man's place in it. Man may be able to harness the power of the atom and make a loud noise and to send space vehicles whirling around the globe. But he has not revoked any of the physical laws which govern the universe—he must still use an old-fashioned parachute to counteract the law of gravity as his space capsule lands. Similarly, although man can shave a forest and dam a stream, he has not repealed the laws that have governed the procession of life upon the planet. He cannot for long toy with the rules that govern ecosystems and communities, that provide built-in balances in the diversity of life around him. Of all the principles of ecology, the primary one was stated in the 17th Century by the philosopher Francis Bacon: "We cannot command nature except by obeying her."

SULPHUR DIOXIDE IN SMELTER FUMES DENUDED THIS MOUNTAIN BEFORE A WAY WAS FOUND TO CONVERT THIS GAS FOR INDUSTRIAL USE

A Growing Awareness

After 10,000 years of exploiting nature, man finds himself in a world molded closely to his needs and desires. But only now is he becoming aware of the consequences of his thoughtless prodigality with natural resources, from the fossil fuels below ground to the soils, the virgin forests and plains and the wildlife. Only now is he beginning to conserve and reclaim natural communities.

171

DUST AND A VARIETY OF CORROSIVE VAPORS ARE SPEWED OUT BY STEEL PLANTS LIKE THIS ONE ON A HIGHWAY ENTERING GARY, INDIANA

The Specter of Pollution

Outrunning the technology and urban societies which spawned them, millions of tons of man-made contaminants are poured into the water we drink and the air we breathe: detergents, pesticides, industrial wastes, exhaust fumes, fly ash and smoke from incinerators, sewage, silt and radioactivity. The problems created by polluted water range from outbreaks of diseases to the destruction of coastal fishing and the disappearance of fish and wildlife along inland waterways. Facing at last the dangers of contamination, the United States, Great Britain and West Germany have taken the lead in long-range programs to counteract them.

Even more critical than water pollution is the wholesale use of the air as a sewer for the products of combustion. London, New York, Chicago and Los Angeles now strictly enforce smog regulations, but despite this, most industrial centers still tolerate toxic levels of gases which take lives, contribute to colds, heart disease and cancer, damage city property and blight farmlands. These evils are partially abated by converting coal-burning furnaces to gas and oil and improving or installing filters not only on smokestacks but on gasoline engines too.

SYNTHETIC SUDS foam down a Chicago drainage canal. Unlike soap, detergents resist bacterial action which might decompose them and may circulate in water supplies for years.

173

A BOUNTY OF PELTS provides evidence of the mass slaughter of coyotes. First hunted as simple predators, they are now receiving new consideration as checks on rabbits and rodents.

The Costly War on Predators

Only slowly does the realization grow that exterminating predators does not solve wildlife problems. Early in the present century man undertook to "protect" an apparently healthy and stable population of about 4,000 mule deer on the Kaibab plateau in Arizona. Not only were the Indians and white settlers barred from hunting deer, but thousands of natural predators—mountain lions, coyotes and wolves—were systematically killed. At the same time, domestic cattle and sheep overgrazed the grasslands, which then grew up into shrub, especially cliff rose, providing abundant browse for deer. Consequently, the deer increased to 100,000 in 1924, the land was overbrowsed, and in the succeeding years thousands of deer starved. By 1939, when they had dropped to 10,000, attempts had been launched to rebuild the natural community —by restoring limited hunting, allowing animal predators to make a comeback, and expanding the range. Today the Kaibab supports 13,000 deer.

Responsible agencies are now opposed to statewide bounties, which cost about two million dollars annually. Instead they advocate carefully administered local programs aimed at controlling predators, but not completely destroying them.

CORNERED IN COLORADO, this mountain lion is one of the last of the big cats, which have steadily declined in number as civilization has encroached on their habitats. Their present

strongholds in North America, besides palmetto forests in Florida, are inaccessible mountain areas in the West, where they live mostly on deer and smaller mammals. Some venture into open rimrock country, however, to prey on domestic herds, and many such are shot by ranchers and professional hunters. Six western states pay high bounties of $50 to $135 for lions.

A MOSAIC PATTERN OF HEDGEROWS, here fencing off cultivated land and meadows in Devon, is repeated throughout England. Each strip contains flora and fauna of the fields and woodlands in an endless variety: stands of elm, oak and ash, and hawthorn intermixed with dogwood, rose and elder, providing a refuge for songbirds, insects and smaller mammals.

The Altered Landscape

Not all man's exploitation of the land he lives on has been destructive to natural communities. In England and Schleswig-Holstein, millions of miles of hedgerows dating back two or three hundred years are not only miniature wildlife sanctuaries, but also prevent erosion, keep the fields moist and supply timber. In the United States, eroded farms have been reclaimed by terracing and planting borders of the luxuriant Asiatic rosebush, *Rosa multiflora*. Besides improving lands already in use, man is tapping ground water to irrigate desert communities *(opposite)* and finding ways to trap surface water in nonarable soils. In Saudi Arabia orange and lemon trees are being grown in a humus formed with the aid of a foam rubber "cushion" under the sand. Another startling advance is the use of one of the desert's own resources—oil—to stabilize sand dunes by spraying them, thus conserving available water and enabling plants to take root on the barrens of North Africa, India, Argentina and Texas.

177

A NEW TOWN RISES IN THE MOJAVE DESERT AS WATER IS BROUGHT FROM DEEP UNDERGROUND TO BRING LIFE TO STERILE DUNES

ON A DOOMED ISLAND, rangers tie up a bushbuck which has been driven into a net. A worldwide appeal brought a large supply of nonchafing rope in the form of nylon stockings.

The Greatest Animal Rescue

When Kariba Dam in southern Africa was sealed in 1958, it created a lake which was to cover 2,000 square miles. Rolling hills became islands where rhinos, elephants and many other mammals and reptiles were stranded. A small group of rangers struggled to save them, equipped only with boats, trapping nets and tireless courage. At the end of the ordeal, they had coaxed, towed or carried more than 6,000 animals to mainland game reserves.

This was "Operation Noah," an enterprise that dramatically underscores a growing concern for Africa's—and all continents'—wildlife. The emergent African nations tend to see game preserves as expendable remnants of colonial rule. But hard economic facts may cause them to reconsider. Wild animals like springbok and impala can be scientifically raised and harvested to feed their protein-starved multitudes, and well-stocked parks are the basis of an annual tourist trade of over $30 million.

A WHIMPERING DUIKER, more terrified of man than the rising lake, is borne through waist-high muck and thorn bush by Rupert Fothergill, director of the Rhodesian rescue operation.

SPED TO FREEDOM in a 20-foot metal boat, wart hogs with bound muzzles calmly snore, but the more nervous antelopes, which struggle if they can see their captors, are blindfolded.

CONSTANT VIGILANCE is still needed to prevent outbreaks of malaria. Here, mosquitoes are collected from the sprayed walls of a home in Iran to test if they are resistant to DDT.

ANTIMALARIAL TABLETS, given to a Liberian woman, may help ward off the disease for a week. Their effectiveness depends on regular use. Longer-lasting drugs are being developed.

MEDIEVAL MAN LINKED MOSQUITOES TO MALARIA

An End to Pestilence

In the past 10 years, there has been a spectacular reduction throughout much of the world in the number of deaths from disease. But in spite of man's best efforts, more than 30,000 people die each year of cholera, nearly 60,000 of smallpox and about two million of man's oldest enemy—malaria. DDT and other insecticides were effective against the various species of *Anopheles* mosquitoes which carry the malaria parasite—for a while. But in less than a decade, mosquitoes began developing a resistance to DDT. This prompted a global campaign in 1955 to break the chain of infection in as many of the infested areas as possible before all the mosquitoes became immune. The World Health Organization's intensive spraying program is supplemented by the administration of synthetic drugs in various forms, which give short-term immunity. Ironically, as successful as these efforts have been, man's triumphs over disease have only intensified his most urgent problem: his explosive population growth. How he can resolve this and maintain the balance of the world ecological community, only the future can tell.

PENETRATING REMOTE JUNGLES of India, U.N. teams attack malaria with insecticides. The World Health Organization program protects half a million people in areas once infected.

Bibliography

General Ecology

*Bates, Marston, *The Forest and the Sea*. Random House, 1960.

*Buchsbaum, Ralph and Mildred, *Basic Ecology*. The Boxwood Press, 1957.

Clarke, George L., *Elements of Ecology*. John Wiley & Sons, 1954.

Dice, Lee R., *Natural Communities*. University of Michigan Press, 1952.

Odum, Eugene P. and Howard T., *Fundamentals of Ecology* (2nd ed.). Saunders, 1959.

Animal Ecology

Allee, W. C., A. E. Emerson, O. Park, T. Park and K. P. Schmidt, *Principles of Animal Ecology*. Saunders, 1949.

Bates, Marston, *Animal Worlds*. Random House, 1963.

*Dowdeswell, W. H., *Animal Ecology* (2nd ed.). Methuen, 1959.

Elton, Charles S., *The Ecology of Animals* (3rd ed.). John Wiley & Sons, 1950.

Kendeigh, S. Charles, *Animal Ecology*. Prentice-Hall, 1961.

Macfadyen, A., *Animal Ecology*. Pitman, 1957.

Plant Ecology

Anderson, Edgar, *Plants, Man and Life*. Little, Brown, 1952.

Daubenmire, R. F., *Plants and Environment* (2nd ed.). John Wiley & Sons, 1959.

Hanson, Herbert C., and Ethan D. Churchill, *The Plant Community*. Reinhold, 1961.

Oosting, Henry J., *The Study of Plant Communities* (2nd ed.). W. H. Freeman, 1956.

Weaver, John E., and Frederic E. Clements, *Plant Ecology* (2nd ed.). McGraw-Hill, 1938.

Ecology of Special Environments

Aubert de la Rüe, Edgar, François Bourlière and Jean-Paul Harroy, *The Tropics*. Alfred A. Knopf, 1957.

*Carson, Rachel, *The Edge of the Sea*. Houghton Mifflin, 1955.

Coker, Robert E., *Streams, Lakes, Ponds*. University of North Carolina Press, 1954.

Dyson, James L., *The World of Ice*. Alfred A. Knopf, 1962.

Farb, Peter, *Living Earth*. Harper & Row, 1959.

Hedgpeth, Joel W., ed., *Treatise on Marine Ecology and Paleoecology*. Geological Society of America, 1957.

McCormick, Jack, *The Living Forest*. Harper & Bros., 1959.

Moore, Hilary B., *Marine Ecology*. John Wiley & Sons, 1958.

Pond, Alonzo W., *The Desert World*. Nelson, 1962.

Reid, George K., *Ecology of Inland Waters and Estuaries*. Reinhold, 1961.

Richards, Paul W., *The Tropical Rain Forest*. Cambridge University Press, 1952.

Ricketts, Edward F., and Jack Calvin, *Between Pacific Tides* (3rd ed., revised by Joel Hedgpeth). Stanford University Press, 1962.

Shelford, V. E., *Ecology of North America*. University of Illinois Press, 1963.

Weaver, J. E., *North American Prairie*. Johnsen, 1954.

Weins, Herold J., *Atoll Environment and Ecology*. Yale University Press, 1962.

Wilson, Douglas P., *Life of the Shore and Shallow Sea*. Nicholson and Watson, 1951.

Yonge, C. M., *The Sea Shore*. Collins, 1949.

Distribution and Abundance of Plants and Animals

Andrewartha, H. G., and L. C. Birch, *The Distribution and Abundance of Animals*. University of Chicago Press, 1954.

Beaufort, L. F. de, *Zoogeography of the Land and Inland Waters*. Sidgwick and Jackson, 1951.

Dansereau, Pierre, *Biogeography*. Ronald, 1957.

Darlington, Phillip J. Jr., *Zoogeography: The Geographical Distribution of Animals*. John Wiley & Sons, 1957.

Elton, Charles S., *The Ecology of Invasions by Animals and Plants*. John Wiley & Sons, 1958.

Hesse, Richard, W. C. Allee and K. P. Schmidt, *Ecological Animal Geography* (2nd ed.). John Wiley & Sons, 1951.

Lack, David, *The Natural Regulation of Animal Numbers*. Oxford University Press, 1954.

Animal Behavior and Adaptations

Allee, W. C., *Cooperation Among Animals*. Abelard-Schuman, 1951.

Cott, Hugh B., *Adaptive Coloration in Animals*. Methuen, 1940.

Dobzhansky, Theodosius, *Mankind Evolving*. Yale University Press, 1962.

*Huxley, Julian, A. C. Hardy and E. B. Ford, eds., *Evolution as a Process* (2nd ed.). Macmillan, 1958.

Klopfer, Peter H., *Behavioral Aspects of Ecology*. Prentice-Hall, 1962.

Mayr, Ernst, *Animal Species and Evolution*. Harvard University Press, 1963.

Scott, John Paul, *Animal Behavior*. University of Chicago Press, 1958.

Tinbergen, Nikolaas, *The Study of Instinct*. Oxford University Press, 1951.

Human Ecology

Bates, Marston, *Man in Nature*. Prentice-Hall, 1961.

*Bates, Marston, *The Prevalence of People*. Scribner, 1955.

†Brown, Harrison, *The Challenge of Man's Future*. Viking Press, 1954.

Dasmann, Raymond F., *The Last Horizon*. Macmillan, 1963.

Dice, Lee, *Man's Nature and Nature's Man: The Ecology of Human Communities*. University of Michigan Press, 1955.

Graham, Edward H., *Natural Principles of Land Use*. Oxford University Press, 1944.

†Malthus, Thomas, Julian Huxley and Frederick Osborn, *Three Essays on Population*. New American Library, 1960.

Milne, Lorus J. and Margery J., *The Balance of Nature*. Alfred A. Knopf, 1960.

Thomas, William L., ed., *Man's Role in Changing the Face of the Earth*. University of Chicago Press, 1956.

Vogt, William, *People? Challenge to Survival*. Sloane, 1960.

Zeuner, Frederick E., *A History of Domesticated Animals*. Hutchinson, 1962.

Miscellaneous

Allen, Durward L., *Our Wildlife Legacy* (rev. ed.). Funk and Wagnalls, 1962.

Bourlière, François, *The Natural History of Mammals*. Alfred A. Knopf, 1954.

Buchsbaum, Ralph, and Lorus J. Milne, *The Lower Animals: Living Invertebrates of the World*. Doubleday, 1960.

Burnet, F. McFarlane, *Natural History of Infectious Diseases* (3rd ed.). Cambridge University Press, 1962.

Collins, Henry Hill, Jr., *Complete Field Guide to American Wildlife*. Harper & Bros., 1959.

Coon, Carleton S., *The Story of Man* (2nd ed., revised). Alfred A. Knopf, 1962.

*Dubos, René, *Mirage of Health*. Harper & Row, 1959.

Gilliard, E. Thomas, *Living Birds of the World*. Doubleday, 1958.

Good, Ronald, *Geography of Flowering Plants* (2nd ed.). Longmans, 1953.

*Hanson, Earl D., *Animal Diversity*. Prentice-Hall, 1961.

Landsberg, Hans H., Leonard L. Fischman and Joseph L. Fisher, *Resources in America's Future*. Johns Hopkins Press, 1963.

Leopold, Aldo, *A Sand County Almanac*. Oxford University Press, 1949.

Milne, Lorus J. and Margery J., *The Biotic World and Man* (2nd ed.). Prentice-Hall, 1958.

Rothschild, Miriam, and Theresa Clay, *Fleas, Flukes & Cuckoos*. Collins, 1952.

Simpson, George Gaylord, Colin S. Pittendrigh and Lewis H. Tiffany, *Life*. Harcourt, Brace & World, 1957.

Welty, Joel Carl, *The Life of Birds*. Alfred A. Knopf, 1963.

*Zinsser, Hans, *Rats, Lice and History*. Little, Brown, 1935.

*Also available in paperback edition.

†Only available in paperback edition.

The Major Biomes of the World

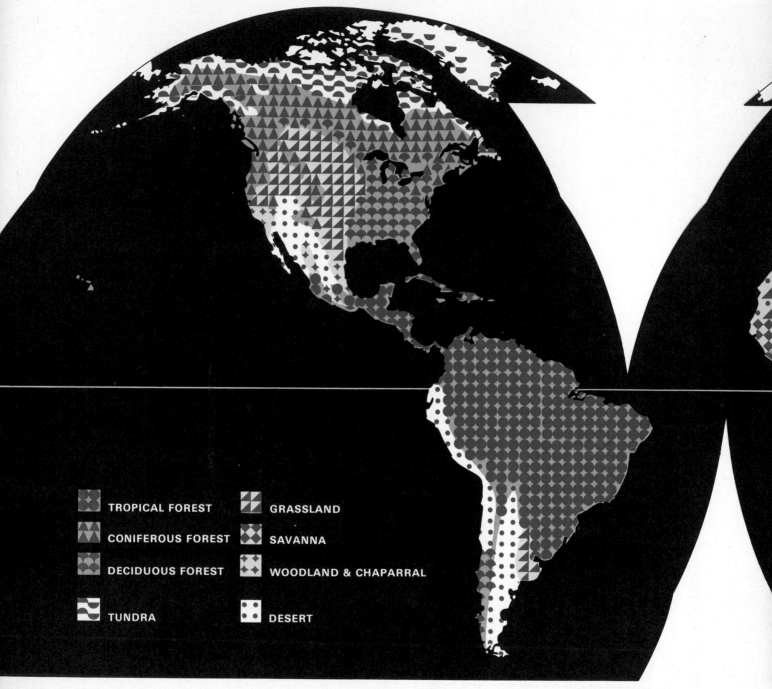

TROPICAL FOREST

CONIFEROUS FOREST

DECIDUOUS FOREST

TUNDRA

GRASSLAND

SAVANNA

WOODLAND & CHAPARRAL

DESERT

This map shows the major biomes of the world as they would be if undisturbed by man. Dark green portions indicate heaviest vegetation—the tropical, temperate and boreal forests. Light greens are open areas of grassland or low trees. White indicates barren lands, arctic or desert. Where one area blends into another, the symbols are mixed. There are nine generally recognized land biomes (two are lumped together here), most of them named for the predom-inant vegetation. In the last analysis, however, it is climate—the basic action of wind, rain and temperature—that molds an environment. For example, in both hemispheres, just beyond the tropics, trade winds blow toward the equator. They carry moisture, which falls in the tropical areas. Thus the tropical forests are created; but to the north and south, these same winds leave behind patches of desert and savanna. Still farther north and south, winds

184

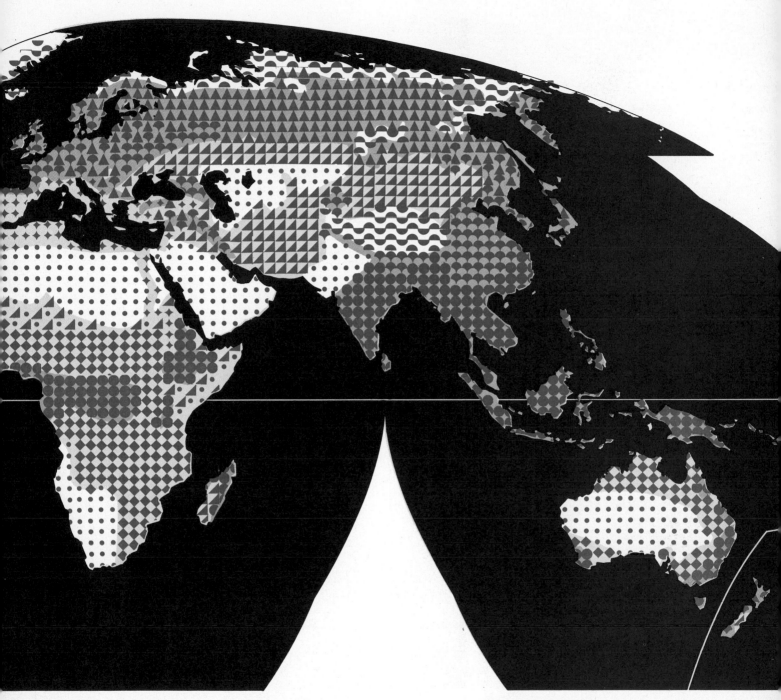

from polar and subtropical zones mix, forming the variable rain patterns that produce the temperate forests and grasslands. Land and ocean also interact in other ways to modify vegetation: aridity, for instance, is characteristic of the interior of Asia because of its distance from the sea. Finally, while biomes are repeated around the world, each continent, as the next pages show, has its own particular version of forest, grassland and the rest, as well as the animals that have adapted themselves to it. Two of the six great zoogeographic realms are sometimes listed as one large region, the Holarctic. Actually, this is made up of two closely related subregions, the Nearctic, or North America, and the Palearctic, or Eurasia. While these are tied together by similarities of climate and probably were once joined at the Bering Strait, they have now been separated long enough to have evolved some differing animal life.

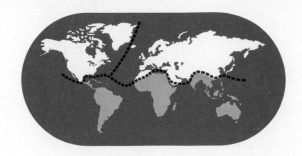

THE NEARCTIC REALM

North America above the tropics, including Newfoundland and Greenland. In the north, snow and ice give way to tundra and a wide belt of coniferous forest. Below are vertical belts of deciduous forests in the east, central grassland, and a western complex of mountains, desert, coniferous forest, woodland and chaparral. Nearctic animals include some that are also common to the Palearctic, some that are endemic, and a few Neotropical forms. Biomes are:

TUNDRA: A low vegetation of lichens, mosses, sedges, scattered herbs and stunted shrubs is characteristic. Its principal faunas are caribou, musk ox, lemmings, arctic hare, arctic fox, wolf, weasels, arctic ground squirrel, polar bear, ptarmigan, snowy owl.
CONIFEROUS FOREST: Typical are dense stands of pine-hemlock, spruce-fir and other needle-leaf trees. Principal faunas are moose, mule deer, porcupine, red-backed mice, snowshoe hare, shrews, wolverine, lynx, wood warblers, woodpeckers, grouse.
GRASSLAND: There are three basic types; true prairie with tall blue stem and Indian grasses, short-grass plains with grama and buffalo grasses, and bunch-grass prairie. Principal faunas are bison, pronghorn, jack rabbit, prairie dog, pocket gopher, badger, fox, coyote. The prairie chicken is a typical bird; among reptiles, the blue racer and rattlesnakes are prevalent.
DECIDUOUS FOREST: These are closed-canopy woods of oak, beech, maple, basswood, with many flowering herbs. Animals include moles, gray and fox squirrels, raccoon, opossum, short-tailed shrew, white-footed mice, chipmunk, white-tailed deer, red fox, black bear, ovenbird, red-eyed vireo.
WOODLAND AND CHAPARRAL: Typical are open stands of piñon-juniper and petran bush and continuous stands of leathery-leaved trees, such as chamiso and manzanita. There are few distinctive animals; most come from nearby biomes.
DESERT: Plants are New World cacti, the saguaro and Joshua trees, plus low shrubs such as sagebrush and creosote bush. The desert annuals are striking in spring. Animals are cottontails, cactus mice, rock and ground squirrels, pocket mice, jack rabbits, kangaroo rat, and many lizards and snakes.

THE PALEARCTIC REALM

All of Eurasia is included, from the British Isles and Ireland eastward to the Bering Strait and south to India and Indochina. Like the Nearctic, the Palearctic has northern belts of ice, tundra and coniferous forest. Temperate parts of China

and Japan have deciduous forest like Europe, but the Asiatic is richer in species. The Asian interior is arid and treeless, characterized by vast areas of steppe and the wastes of the Gobi Desert. Palearctic animals are closely allied to Nearctic species in the north, but southward the Palearctic blends off into Oriental-related forms. Main biomes are:

TUNDRA: In both flora and fauna it is not significantly different from the Nearctic.
CONIFEROUS FOREST: The same genera of trees—pine, fir, spruce—as are found in the Nearctic, but different species. The same applies to animals—i.e., lynx, wolverine, moose.
GRASSLAND: Grass types here are similar to the Nearctic. Typical animals: saiga and Tibetan antelope, goitered gazelle, wild ass, horse and camel; also, European ground squirrel, hamster, Asiatic jerboa, weasels, jackal, corsac fox.
DECIDUOUS FOREST: This is predominantly beech, maple, oak, hornbeam, basswood of distinct species. Many animals are equivalent to those of the Nearctic.
WOODLAND AND CHAPARRAL: An area around the Mediterranean is similar to the Nearctic equivalent and like it forms an ecotone where animals from other communities mix.
DESERT: Characteristic is a sparse cover of low sagebrush, clumps of wiry grass, thorny bushes called camel sage, and zag, turai, tamarisk and cottonwood trees. Some grazers are here, plus hedgehog, jerboas, sand rat, voles, hamsters, eagle, hawk, owl.

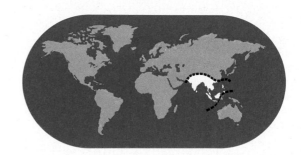

THE ORIENTAL REALM

This includes India and Indochina, with Ceylon, Sumatra, Java, Borneo, Formosa and the Philippines. Lush forest covers the islands, but the mainland is split by mountains, many with a rich and varied plant cover, which in western India give way to dry plains. Of all the tropical regions, it has the fewest unique species, the Orient as a whole having been a center of origin and dispersal for vertebrates. Its faunas most resemble the Ethiopian. Predominant biome:

TROPICAL FOREST: Here, as in all tropical forests, hundreds of plant species may be found crowded together in rich profusion. Some typical ones: snake plant, bamboo, Manila hemp and teak, banyan and ebony trees. The area is rich in primates: gibbons, orangutan, the Old World monkeys, and small monkey relatives—tree shrews, tarsier, lorises. Also characteristic: Indian elephant, tapir, two kinds of rhinoceroses, porcupine, tiger, sloth bear and sun bear, deer and antelopes. There are many pheasants, poisonous snakes and a variety of lizards.

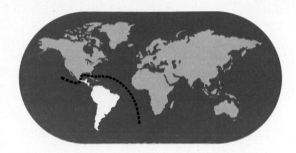

THE NEOTROPICAL REALM

South and Central America, tropical Mexico and the Caribbean islands are included here. Continental South America has vast stretches of tropical forest and grassland, but parts of it, as well as of Central America, have some of the world's most complex vegetation confined to a small area. The fauna of this realm, because of its long isolation, is most distinctive, particularly in the rodent forms. Main biomes are:

TROPICAL FOREST: Half the continent is covered with tropical forest uniquely rich in epiphytes—lichens, mosses, orchids, bromeliads. Plants include cabbage palm, tree fern, almendro tree, bamboo, lianas. Small animals abound: New World monkeys, kinkajou, pygmy anteater, coati, sloth, small deer, paca, agouti, ocelot, mouse opossums, lizards; also tree snakes, many parrots and hummingbirds.
GRASSLAND: This is a mixture of pampas, ichu, needle, blue stem and chloris grasses. Animal life: guanaco, rhea, pampas deer, plains viscacha, pampas cavy, tuco tuco, pampas cat, South American foxes, hog-nosed skunks, tinamous, swallows, burrowing owl.
DESERT: Much of this is wind-swept waste with scanty bunch grass, low bushes, cacti, yucca, creosote bush, sagebrush, agave, cereus. Animals are the guanaco, rhea, armadillos, vulture, fox, Patagonian "hare," tuco tuco.

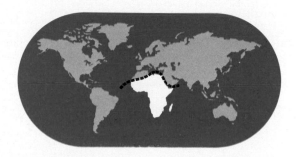

THE ETHIOPIAN REALM

Africa except for its northwestern corner comprises the largest part, plus Madagascar and southern Arabia. West Africa, along the equator, is covered with tropical forest, as are the mountain areas of East Africa. Much of the rest of the central continent is savanna and grassland, merging into the Sahara in the north and the Kalahari in the southwest. On this continent is the world's finest example of tropical savanna, with its remarkable herds of grazing ungulates. Some of these mammals are found nowhere else. In general the animal life of this realm shows more relationships to the Oriental than to any other region. Principal biomes are:

TROPICAL FOREST: This is the most restricted of tropical forests. Hardwoods such as mahogany are typical; also rubber tree, ferns, lianas, and orchids and other epiphytes. Animals include the royal antelope, okapi, pygmy hippopotamus, lowland gorilla, chimpanzees, guenons and bishop monkeys, forest elephant.
SAVANNA: Essentially a grassland area, it is dotted with trees like the acacia, baobab, euphorbia, doom palm. The grazers: zebras, elands, gemsbok, hartebeests, gnus, etc.; also typical: giraffes, bush elephant, ostrich, black and white rhinoceroses, lion, wart hog, cheetah, Cape hunting dog, ground squirrels, golden mole.
DESERT: Vegetation is chiefly scanty clumps of grass and bushes, with date palms in the oases, and, in the south, Welwitschia, euphorbias and plants with tuberous roots. Faunas include springbok, porcupine, jerboa, gundi, rock hyrax, tenrec, eagle, lizards.

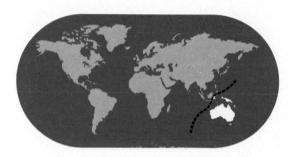

THE AUSTRALIAN REALM

Sometimes known as Australasia, this includes Australia, Tasmania, New Guinea, New Zealand and the South Pacific islands. Australia's central core of desert is surrounded by savanna and grassland, with scattered patches of tropical forest. The other islands vary from the lush forests of New Guinea to cool-temperate New Zealand. Connecting land bridges disappeared many ages ago, creating an isolated island realm with a unique plant and mammal population. Pouched marsupials—and flightless birds—take over the niches filled by placental mammals elsewhere. Its biomes are:

DESERT: Characteristic vegetation is saltbush and bluebush, acacia, eucalyptus and river red gum trees. The animals are marsupial mole, jumping mouse, "jerboa" rat, spiny devil lizard, parakeets.
SAVANNA: This is typically grassland and woodland, including such trees as red stringybark, jarrah, wallum, ironbark, yellow box, white box, coolibah. Besides the red kangaroo and emu, there are pig-footed and rabbit bandicoots, wombats, cockatoos, parrots.
TROPICAL FOREST: This consists of closed-canopy rain forest, with vines and lianas, or open eucalyptus forest, with mountain ash and stunted gum trees. Marsupials include the Forester, tree and musk kangaroos, wallabies, koala, opossums, marsupial wolf, Tasmanian devil, platypus, flying foxes, cassowary, lyrebird.

187

Credits

Credits for pictures from left to right are separated by commas, top to bottom by dashes.

Cover—N. R. Farbman
8—Andreas Feininger
11—maps by Mark A. Binn
12—drawing by Eric Gluckman
15—drawing by Otto van Eersel
17—Dr. Edward S. Ross from California Academy of Science
18 through 21—paintings by Otto van Eersel
22, 23—William W. Bacon III from Rapho-Guillumette, Josef Muench
24—Charles E. Rotkin from Photography for Industry
25—Dmitri Kessel
26, 27—top Keith Gillett; bottom Dmitri Kessel, Russ Kinne from Photo Researchers, Inc.
28—N. R. Farbman
29—Fritz Goro
30, 31—Eliot Elisofon
32, 33—Fritz Goro
34—Dr. Douglas P. Wilson
37—drawing by Otto van Eersel
40, 41—drawing by Guy Tudor
43—drawing by Matt Greene
45—Dr. Douglas P. Wilson
46, 47—paintings by Jack J. Kunz, M. A. Wilson (2), Dr. Douglas P. Wilson—Dr. Douglas P. Wilson
48, 49—Dr. Douglas P. Wilson except top right; drawing by Jack J. Kunz
50—drawing by Jack J. Kunz—Dr. Douglas P. Wilson
51, 52, 53—Dr. Douglas P. Wilson
54—George Silk
56, 57—drawings by Louis Darling
59—drawing by Jack J. Kunz

60—drawings by Rudolf Freund
61—drawing by Otto van Eersel
63—Eliot Elisofon
64, 65—paintings by Jack J. Kunz
66—Walter Dawn
67—Virgil Argo
68, 69—David Attenborough
70—Australian Scientific and Industrial Research Organization
71—Paul Almasy
72, 73—H. Goldstein, Harry Pennington, Jr.
74—Fritz Goro
77, 78, 79—drawings by Otto van Eersel
80—drawing by René Martin
83—Professor Dr. Bernhard Grzimek
84, 85—Theodore Brauner
86, 87—Cy La Tour, University of California; Department of Zoology—Academy Films
88—left C. K. Bartell; right William H. Amos
89, 90, 91—Fritz Goro
92—Marshall Lockman from Black Star
93—James Drake
94—Miriam Rothschild
96—drawing by Louis Darling
99—drawing by René Martin
101—drawing by Rudolf Freund
103—drawing by Rudolf Freund
105—Henry B. Kane
106 through 109—Shelley Grossman
110—Stephen Collins from Photo Researchers, Inc., Constance P. Warner—W. H. Hodge, Dr. Ross E. Hutchins—R. Jay Smith, Walter Dawn

111—Constance P. Warner, Dr. Edward S. Ross from California Academy of Science, William H. Amos—Dr. Paul F. Sand, W. H. Hodge, Dr. Edward S. Ross from California Academy of Science—Walter Dawn, Eric V. Grave (2)
112—Douglas Faulkner—T. J. Walker
113—Douglas Faulkner
114, 115—Stephen Collins, Hermann Eisenbeiss from Photo Researchers, Inc.
116—Walter Dawn
117—George Silk—James Simon from Photo Researchers, Inc.
118, 119—J. R. Eyerman
120—Dr. E. S. Ross from California Academy of Science
123—drawings by René Martin
124—drawing by Louis Darling
125—drawing by Rudolf Freund
126—drawing by René Martin
127—drawing by Matt Greene
129—Dr. E. S. Ross from California Academy of Science
130, 131—Constance P. Warner
132, 133—Charles E. Mohr from National Audubon Society except bottom left; Russ Kinne from Photo Researchers, Inc.
134—Douglas B. Evans except left; Dr. Ross E. Hutchins
135—John Gerard from Monkmeyer Press Photos
136, 137—drawing by Matt Greene
138, 139—George Rodger from Magnum

140—Carroll Seghers II from Black Star
143—drawings by Eric Gluckman
145—drawing by Guy Tudor
149—drawing by Otto van Eersel
151—George Silk
152 through 155—paintings by Rudolf Freund
156—Andreas Feininger
157—Culver Pictures
158—Culver Pictures except bottom; The Bettmann Archive, Brown Brothers
159—Brown Brothers except top; Smithsonian Institution bottom right; New York Zoological Society photo
160, 161—Carl Iwasaki—Loomis Dean
162—Margaret Bourke-White
164 drawing by René Martin
167—drawing by Matt Greene
168—drawing by Otto van Eersel
169—drawings by Matt Greene
171—U.S. Forest Service
172—Arthur Shay for TIME
173—Francis Miller
174, 175—Carl Iwasaki
176—Ralph Crane
177—Val Doone
178, 179—Terence Spencer
180, 181—Courtesy World Health Organization
182, 183—Copyright by Rand McNally & Company, R. L. 63s94
184, 185—map by Elton Robinson
186, 187—maps by Adolph E. Brotman
Back Cover—Matt Greene

Acknowledgments

The editors of this book are particularly indebted to S..Charles Kendeigh, Professor of Zoology, University of Illinois, who read the book in its entirety. The editors are also indebted to David V. Aldrich, Bureau of Commercial Fisheries, U.S. Department of the Interior; William H. Amos; Chris Angelidis, Sanitary Engineer, Gary Department of Health, Gary, Indiana; Vernon C. Applegate, U.S. Fish and Wildlife Service, Fisheries Biology, Great Lakes Project, University of Michigan; Stanley I. Auerbach, Chief, Radiation Ecology Station, Health Physics Division, Oak Ridge National Laboratory; Richard A. Boolootian, Department of Zoology, University of California; Harry A. Borthwick, Chief Plant Physiologist, Crops Research Division, U.S. Department of Agriculture; Leslie A. Braby; Robert B. Branstead, Soil Conservation Service, U.S. Department of Agriculture; Theodore Brauner; Frank Brown, Professor of Biology, Northwestern University; Richard D. Clemens, California State Agriculture Bureau; William C. Cobb, Director of Publications, Rockefeller Foundation; Stephen Collins; C. Earl Cooley, Doubleday and Co., Inc.; James Crayhon, Public Relations Department, Standard Oil Co. (N.J.); Spencer H. Davis, College of Agriculture, New Brunswick, New Jersey; R. W. Decker, Associate Professor of Geology, Dartmouth College; James T. Enright, Max Planck Institut Für Verhaltenphysiologie, Erling-Anechs, OBB, West Germany; Douglas B. Evans, Big Bend National Park, Texas; Roland Force, Director, Bernice P. Bishop Museum, Honolulu, Hawaii; Ira N. Gabrielson, World Wildlife Fund; Eric Grave; Leonard Greenbaum, Assistant to the Director, Michigan Memorial-Phoenix Project, University of Michigan; John N. Hamlet; Julian L. Hayes, Publicity Manager, The Anaconda Co.; Brian Hocking, Head, Department of Entomology, University of Alberta; S. H. Hutner, Haskins Laboratory; Jean M. Ingersoll, Hudson Institute; Charles Edwin Jenner; Adrian B. Jones; Allen Keast, Department of Biology, Queen's University, Kingston, Ontario; W. Bryce Kendrick, Mycologist-Ecologist; Thomas L. Kimball, Executive Director, National Wildlife Federation; John A. King, Associate Professor of Zoology, Michigan State University; Wallace Kirkland; Richard Klein, Curator of Plant Physiology, New York Botanical Garden; Glenn C. Klingman, Professor of Crop Science, School of Agriculture, North Carolina State College; Alexander B. Klots, Professor of Biology, The City College of New York; James Larson, Academy Films; Vernon G. MacKenzie, Division of Air Pollution, U.S. Department of Health, Education and Welfare; Thomas A. Manar, Publications-Public Information, University of California, San Diego; Ruth Mecklenburg, World Health Organization; Ken Middleham; David W. Miller, Water Information Center, Inc.; Mr. and Mrs. Josef Muench; Brother G. Nicholas, F.S.C., LaSalle College, Philadelphia; Carl H. Oppenheimer, The Marine Laboratory, University of Miami, Miami, Florida; Willis E. Pequegnat; Dennis Pileston, Head, Information Division, Brookhaven National Laboratory, Associated Universities, Inc.; Robert B. Platt, Professor of Biology, Emory University; Leland J. Prater, Forest Service, U.S. Department of Agriculture; Dorothy Reville, Photographic Librarian, New York Zoological Park; Jack Richard; Miriam Rothschild; Armand Rotonda, American Forest Products Industries; Paul F. Sand, In Charge, Witchweed Laboratory, Plant Pest Division, Agriculture Research Service, U.S. Department of Agriculture; Edward J. Schantz, Fort Detrick, Frederick, Maryland; Harper Simms, Soil Conservation Service, U.S. Department of Agriculture; Mrs. G. C. Smith, Genetics Research Unit, Carnegie Institution; R. Jay Smith, Associate Professor of Biology, University of Detroit; Arthur C. Stern, Division of Air Pollution, U.S. Department of Health, Education and Welfare; Laura Thompson, Anthropology Department, San Francisco State College; William L. Vaught, Soil Conservation Service, U.S. Department of Agriculture; Constance P. Warner; William E. Waters, Division of Forest Insect Research, U.S. Department of Agriculture; John Waugh, Allied Chemical Corp.; Paul Webb, Game Management Biologist, Arizona Game and Fish Department; F. W. Went, Director, Missouri Botanical Garden; Elizabeth Wiederman, Publications, Rockefeller Foundation; M. Woodbridge Williams, National Park Service; Thomas F. Williams, Division of Air Pollution, Department of Health, Education and Welfare; Robert Woodward, National Audubon Society; George Woodwell, Ecosystem Division, Brookhaven National Laboratory, Associated Universities, Inc.; Noel Wygant, Rocky Mountain Experiment Station, Fort Collins, Colorado.

Index

*Numerals in italics indicate a photograph
or painting of the subject mentioned.*

PRODUCTION STAFF FOR TIME INCORPORATED

Arthur R. Murphy Jr. (Vice President and Director of Production), Robert E. Foy, James P. Menton and Caroline Ferri
Text photocomposed under the direction of Albert J. Dunn and Arthur J. Dunn

✕

Printed by R. R. Donnelley & Sons Company, Crawfordsville, Indiana,
and by Livermore and Knight Co., a division of Printing Corporation of America, Providence, Rhode Island
Bound by R. R. Donnelley & Sons Company, Crawfordsville, Indiana
Paper by The Mead Corporation, Dayton, Ohio